NEVER

HOPE

The Little Girl Who Changed The World

Katie Fasciano

Meaningful Books Publishing

Never Give Up Hope: The Little Girl Who Changed The World
By Katie Fasciano

Published by Meaningful Books Publishing
Westwood, New Jersey, USA

www.seimeihealing.com

Contact publisher for bulk orders and permission requests.

Printed in the United States of America.

Library of Congress Control Number: 2023908474

ISBN (Hardcover):   979-8-9881583-0-1
ISBN (Paperback):   979-8-9881583-1-8
ISBN (Kindle):   979-8-9881583-2-5

Table of Contents

Introduction

I dedicate this book to the loving memory of my daughter Elizabeth. It is a story of faith, hope, love, support, and healing. In Elizabeth's short time in this world, she made sure to share her love wherever she went.

I learned many things about the strength and determination of an incredible little girl in this journey. I met many people and communities that gave me hope and support even in the darkest moments. I will never forget these things.

Later in Elizabeth's journey, I found the Seimei community. The love and dedication shown by this community were priceless.

When you read this book, think of the good times and remember never to give up hope. I wish for your journey through life to be an easier one. Elizabeth was an inspiration to all who met her, and I hope she continues to be through the story that unfolds on these pages.

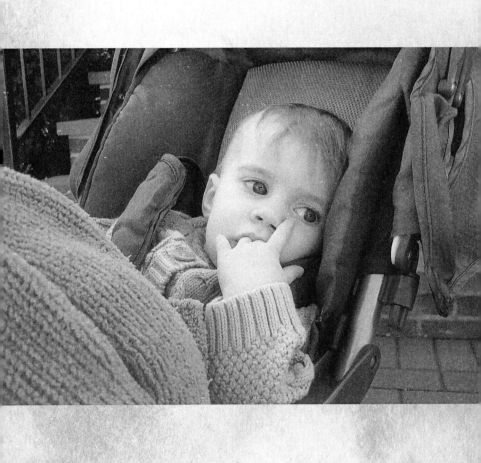

CHAPTER ONE

My Baby Girl

Elizabeth was my first baby. The moment she came into this world was like no moment before. I had a good pregnancy despite the extra weight and swelling. I was due the day after Mother's Day. I wondered whether I was considered a mother yet. I figured I was because I had been pregnant for nine months and was about to deliver the baby.

My doctor induced me overnight when I was nine days late. The next morning, the doctor told me that I had only dilated one centimeter. They would probably have to induce me again that night. They decided to give Pitocin a try first to start the labor. The Pitocin intensified everything. I decided to get the epidural without realizing the intensification was from Pitocin. It was a bit of a bummer because I had gone through Lamaze. I had prepared to work through the labor pain with my breath.

Luckily, the Pitocin started to work. Within a few hours, I was ten centimeters dilated. After pushing for half an hour, I delivered my baby. They put her on my chest. I was overwhelmed by the love I felt. She was perfect! They whisked her away for the standard testing and declared her a perfectly healthy baby.

I began nursing Elizabeth right away. She latched on without a problem. Later in the evening, Elizabeth wasn't content. The nursing didn't seem to calm her. The nurse came in and told me that my milk had not come in yet. The first few days after I gave birth, my body produced colostrum. Since colostrum wasn't like regular breastmilk, Elizabeth was hungry. The nurse gave

Elizabeth formula. I felt like I had failed. Did this mean I would never be able to nurse Elizabeth? Oh, the jitters of being a first-time mom. Thankfully Elizabeth only needed the supplement for a brief time.

Two days later, her dad and I brought her home. Some family members came over to support us. We thought we knew what was to come as we ventured into parenthood.

As we settled in with our newborn, we saw a rainbow in the sky. This was significant to us! You only see rainbows every once in a while.

We took her to church only a week and a half into her life. I was looking in the bulletin, and I saw there was an Elizabeth Ministry. I thought, *Oh! How exciting! A ministry with her name.* I was curious about what this ministry was for, so I read about it. It was for parents that had lost a child through miscarriage or infant death.

I thought, *Oh my gosh, did I give my daughter the wrong name? Is she going to die?* I felt that was a premonition of what was going to happen.

I took Elizabeth to a trial music class at two months old. I thought she was way too young to get benefits out of it. Well, I was wrong. She bounced along to the rhythm of the music. Wow! She liked the classes at such a young age. I was so glad my cousin told me about it. I signed Elizabeth up right away.

A few months later, Elizabeth met her first friend in music class. Her friend's mom and I both worked at corporate jobs. I had just returned to work. Her friend's mom was returning to work soon after we met. We hit it off right away. We both were first-time moms and shared lots of similarities. No matter what, we always found time for our girls to be together. A solid friendship ensued.

Instead of sucking her thumb, Elizabeth sucked on her ring and middle fingers. This was the same way you held your fingers in sign language to say, "I love you." My sweet girl was already sharing her love with the world.

Elizabeth met all her typical milestones in development. She learned to crawl at five months old. She had solid foods at five and a half months old. She took her first unassisted steps at eleven months old. She spoke a few words when she was one.

Her dad and I took her to Chuck E. Cheese for her first birthday. Elizabeth loved going to Chuck E. Cheese. All the lights and sounds fascinated her. She got to eat pizza and drink soda. Oh, what fun we all had!

The following weekend, we had a small birthday party with her grandparents, aunt, and uncle. Elizabeth had macaroni and cheese, meatloaf, and broccoli for dinner. Everything was perfectly normal until a month later.

CHAPTER TWO

The First Battle

July 12, 2006

There was nothing unique about this morning. Elizabeth was in her highchair eating her breakfast. She was smiling as she always did, enjoying her cereal and fruit. Her babysitter Laura arrived so I could leave for work. Laura had just started babysitting Elizabeth the day before. Usually, Elizabeth's nana would watch her, but that week she was on vacation.

I arrived at my corporate job as usual. I had a conference call first thing in the morning. Soon after I jumped on my call, I heard from Laura. Receiving a call from Laura was unusual because she hadn't called the day before. There was an urgency in her voice. She said Elizabeth had taken a fall. I asked where this had happened. She said it took place in the family room, on the padded carpet, while Elizabeth was coasting along the couch. Elizabeth was only thirteen months old and a new walker, so I told Laura not to worry. I felt Elizabeth would be fine, but Laura insisted I come home. I didn't see any urgency to the situation, so I told Laura that I would finish my conference call first. Laura agreed, and I went back to my call.

An hour later, Laura called again. She said Elizabeth was feeling better and was about to take a nap. I told her great and that I would speak to her later.

Another ninety minutes passed, and then Laura called once more. This time Laura's voice had an urgent tone again. Laura had put Elizabeth in her crib for her nap. Since she was still worried about Elizabeth, she decided to stay in Elizabeth's room and watch her while she slept. After about an hour, Laura left the room. She returned soon after to find out that Elizabeth had thrown up in her crib.

Upon hearing this, I knew something was wrong. Elizabeth had only thrown up a couple of times in her life. I immediately got off my conference call and headed home. I called the pediatrician's office. They said that they were leaving for lunch but to still bring her in right away. Thankfully my job was close to home.

When I arrived home, Elizabeth reached for me. When she got into my arms, she started to fall back to sleep. She had just taken a nap and shouldn't have been sleepy. My concern was growing. I asked Laura to come with me in the car. I had her sit in the back seat with Elizabeth. I was nervous that Elizabeth would throw up again and I didn't want her to choke. Laura agreed to come with us.

Ambulance Ride

We were taken straight to an examination room when we arrived at the doctor's office. The nurse came in to take a look at Elizabeth. Soon afterward, Elizabeth's doctor came in, followed by the three other doctors. They observed Elizabeth and measured her head. They didn't comment on the measurement, but they asked me which hospital I wanted for Elizabeth. There were a few hospitals close by. I chose Valley Hospital, but I didn't understand why we needed to go there. My fear grew as I wondered what in the world could be wrong.

The doctors agreed with my hospital choice since there might be trauma to Elizabeth's brain. They felt Valley Hospital would be better equipped to handle it. They told me that an ambulance was on the way. Now my panic intensified. I called Elizabeth's dad and updated him. He remained calm and said it was probably just a routine test. His calmness helped me. I asked Laura to come along in the ambulance with us. She agreed, thankfully.

Before the ambulance arrived, the staff brought Laura into a different room. A police officer questioned her. When the police officer finished with Laura, he asked questions of me too. He asked if Elizabeth had gotten into the medicine cabinet or into some cleaning supplies. I answered no. He also asked if I trusted Laura. I said I did. The police officer needed to rule out foul play.

Emergency Surgery

Off we went to Valley Hospital. They whisked Elizabeth into a pediatric emergency room (ER). Laura asked to see her mother, who worked at the hospital. I said yes. Laura had been through a lot. I was happy that she could find comfort at that time.

I stood next to Elizabeth as she lay in her hospital bed. The staff was trying to start an IV. She was fighting the process. Eventually, they asked me to leave the room. I was devastated to have to go. I understood why, but I never wanted to leave Elizabeth's side. I wish there could have been a different way. I was scared and had no idea what was going on. The last thing I wanted to do was to let Elizabeth be on her own with the medical staff. She was scared too.

The staff took me into a different room so I could call my family. I began sobbing as I made the first call. They said that I could no longer make calls. They were concerned that if I did, people could get into a car accident as they rushed to get there. Instead, they asked for the phone numbers and called for me.

Elizabeth had a CT scan. When the scan finished, the medical staff told me my daughter probably had a brain tumor.

I sat alone, trying to take that in.

The following person that walked into the room leaned forward and shook my hand. She said, "Hello, I'm your daughter's neurosurgeon." I was thinking, *What is going on?*

The doctor asked where Elizabeth's dad was. I said I didn't know, so the doctor called him. Elizabeth's dad said he was stuck in traffic due to the rainy weather. The doctor told me to follow her upstairs.

The medical staff took Elizabeth upstairs on a gurney. The doctor explained that Elizabeth needed an emergency MRI. I still didn't understand what was happening.

A priest came and gave Elizabeth her last rites. Again, I thought, *What is going on?* The doctor explained that Elizabeth needed emergency surgery. *Oh my gosh, how could this be happening?* I thought.

Finally, Elizabeth's dad arrived. Now he and I were sitting across from the doctor. She was trying to bring him up to speed. She said our daughter had a 50/50 chance of surviving surgery. Hearing this was when I lost it.

I started crying convulsively. The medical staff got me a wheelchair. I was caving into myself and then sitting back up and caving again. There was no end to the depth of my sorrow. Someone told me to get it together. I said, "There is no getting it together. The doctor told me I might not have my baby later today."

We had a brief moment to see our daughter right before her emergency surgery. I thought, *Will I ever see her alive again?*

A long five hours ensued. The medical staff let us stay in a tiny playroom in the pediatric intensive care unit (PICU) while we waited for Elizabeth's surgery to be done. The extended family came with food and offered their support. We tried to make small talk, but nothing would take away that deep ache we all felt.

We finally got the call saying Elizabeth had made it through surgery. There was a shared sense of relief in the room. Now we waited again. She was in the recovery room. Finally, the medical staff brought Elizabeth to her PICU room.

She was in a crib with many tubes and cords attached to her. Her head had gauze wrapped around it. They had her in an induced coma due to the trauma of the surgery. During surgery she was bleeding, so they had done multiple blood transfusions. Her body eventually reached a point where it couldn't handle any more blood transfusions. This caused doctors to stop the surgery.

Elizabeth's neurosurgeon said she had gotten about seventy-five percent of the tumor out. We were grateful but had hoped for one hundred percent. The preliminary results led doctors to believe Elizabeth's tumor was a primitive neuro-ectodermal tumor (PNET), which was highly malignant.

It was tough seeing Elizabeth hooked up to so many medical devices. Seeing her like this gave us a preview of what was to come. Her dad and I stayed with Elizabeth in the hospital. Thankfully she made it through the first night.

July 13, 2006

Elizabeth stayed in her induced coma. We were with Elizabeth all day. My job was very understanding. They didn't pressure me to come back to work. Elizabeth's dad had flexibility with his job too. The hospital staff made our next overnight stay more comfortable. They had a sleep study room that they offered to us. Another mom from the PICU complained that we were getting special accommodations. She had no idea why this was happening. Thankfully her child wasn't as critical as our daughter.

Elizabeth's dad and I took turns staying in Elizabeth's PICU room. For the couple of hours that I was in a separate room, I crashed from exhaustion.

July 14, 2006

Doctors woke Elizabeth from her induced coma on the third day after surgery. The day shift nurse ran a strict shift. We made sure we didn't get in her way. The night shift nurse had a softer approach. She called to have a regular hospital bed brought into Elizabeth's room. She had me lay down in the hospital bed.

She lifted Elizabeth from the crib and laid her down on my chest. It was like I had given birth to my baby all over again. I hadn't known if I would ever have the chance to hold her again. It was one of the best gifts of my life.

The same day shift nurse was working the next day. She got the crib back and put Elizabeth in it. I was not happy about it, but I managed to be apart from my daughter. Thank goodness the same night shift nurse was back that evening. She once again ordered the hospital bed. She brought Elizabeth back to me in bed. She said she would make sure that Elizabeth would stay in that bed. As the nurses' shifts changed, she told the day nurse to let the hospital bed stay. Thankfully the bed stayed.

The final pathology of Elizabeth's tumor came back. It wasn't a PNET but rather a choroid plexus carcinoma (CPC). CPC is a very rare and highly malignant tumor. We started looking for children's cancer hospitals to help our daughter. Our extended family was able to stay with Elizabeth while we were visiting cancer centers.

We visited Hackensack University Medical Center (HUMC) first. We walked into Tomorrow's Children's Institute at HUMC. The staff gave us a tour. My heart felt like it was being ripped out of my chest to see children undergoing treatment. It was beyond devastating to think our daughter might be doing the same thing soon.

Next, we met with the pediatric neuro-oncologist. This doctor had been trained at Memorial Sloan Kettering and worked at St. Jude Children's Research Hospital. He said, "There's only one Elizabeth, and we're aiming for one hundred percent." Her tumor was stage four, so we had to act quickly. The doctor wanted to use a cancer protocol named Head Start III for Elizabeth.

A Second Opinion

We went to get a second opinion at a New York City (NYC) hospital. The pediatric neuro-oncologist said, "Here is the choroid plexus carcinoma." The doctor was excited because he usually only saw one patient with CPC a year. It wasn't a good start for us. Our daughter was not her disease. She was Elizabeth. We didn't appreciate that the doctor didn't refer to her by her name.

The pediatric neuro-oncologist told us their hospital does the Head Start III cancer protocol more frequently, so they were better at it. The cancer world was new to us, so we didn't know what to believe. We did notice that the NYC hospital had multiple beds in one room, whereas HUMC had private rooms for all the children. We also realized how much further the NYC hospital was away from us. We asked what would happen if she spiked a fever. They said we would go to a local hospital. We were worried that the local hospital didn't have our daughter's prior history to treat her most effectively. Also, would the medical staff know how to access her central line? Would they keep her away from other patients since her immune system would be compromised?

We chose HUMC to proceed with Elizabeth's cancer treatment. Our decision was easy once Elizabeth's pediatric neurosurgeon recommended the doctor from HUMC. We brought our extended family to meet Elizabeth's pediatric neuro-oncologist. The second time we went to HUMC was not as bad as the first time.

A social worker named Greg, also known as Oreo, gave us a tour of the pediatric inpatient hematology/oncology (HEM/ONCO) floor. As we passed the Procedures Room, we asked Greg what they did in this room. His response was procedures. We all had a good laugh. We found out later that this was Greg's first day on the job. He honestly had no clue about the room. Later, Greg signed his name in front of us. It looked like Oreo, so this was how his nickname stuck. We would buy Oreos for him whenever we got a chance. It helped us to laugh and joke during this stressful time. Greg was a good sport.

Our extended family supported our decision to go to HUMC for Elizabeth's cancer treatment. Now was the waiting game. Elizabeth's tumor was very aggressive. Her pediatric neuro-oncologist said we would start the cancer protocol as soon as she got cleared by the pediatric neurosurgeon. Elizabeth spent ten days in the PICU. She spent another two weeks home before the surgeon discharged her.

The medical staff suggested cutting her hair short. They said it would not be as hard on us when her hair fell out. We went along with the suggestion and got her hair cut.

Physical Therapy

When the medical staff took Elizabeth out of the induced coma, they saw paralysis on the right side of her body. The medical staff quickly called to have a physical therapist do an evaluation.

The staff said, "Oh, you want Lisa as your daughter's physical therapist. She lost a child." There was a possibility that I might lose my child, so I took the opportunity for Lisa to work with my daughter. She knew the pain that we might feel one day.

Lisa had been through a long battle with her youngest daughter, who had a rare genetic disease. Lisa knew the pain of watching her child suffer. I had hoped that Elizabeth would survive, but I knew I could go to Lisa for support if she died. We were blessed to have Lisa in our life.

During the first physical therapy session I saw that Lisa was an absolute angel. She had such a tender and caring way about her. Lisa always wore a necklace with a picture of her sweet daughter. During her assessment of Elizabeth's paralysis she showed me something.

Lisa said, "Look at this. When you do this with her arm, Elizabeth reacts. I don't know how long this will take, but I feel she can regain her mobility." It was only a slight movement, but it showed a reaction. Elizabeth had some sensation in her nerve endings on that side of her body to be able to react to the light touch. During that first physical therapy session, Lisa had given us more hope.

Lisa started seeing Elizabeth for therapy during the rest of her hospital stay. After Elizabeth was released, we took her to Valley Hospital's Center for Child Development. We were lucky to continue to have Lisa as Elizabeth's physical therapist. Elizabeth also began occupational therapy, and soon after, speech therapy.

A beautiful thing Lisa did was to start a foundation for her daughter, the Mary Therese Rose Fund. She invited my daughter to participate in a program called Saturday Stars. On Saturday mornings, Elizabeth would go to the program.

Elizabeth got to dance in a group with the other kids. She also learned to play the piano, among other things.

Our family gave back to the Mary Therese Rose Fund by attending their annual fundraising dinner. We would also participate in their silent auction. Since Elizabeth was participating in Saturday Stars, she danced at the fundraiser. It brought the whole room to tears of joy. Elizabeth and the other children kept the show going no matter what. The audience was hugely enthusiastic. There was always wild applause for each child. It was a fantastic way to give back.

Hippotherapy

We found out about hippotherapy through Lisa. Hippotherapy is physical, occupational, or speech therapy provided while the patient is riding a horse. A wonderful thing about hippotherapy is that the horse's movements are similar to that of a human. Because of this, it helped the rider's compromised body to relearn how to move correctly. Rehabbing Elizabeth's right-sided paralysis was the reason she went to hippotherapy.

We started hippotherapy for Elizabeth as soon as possible. They assigned Paula to us. She was an occupational therapist and another angel in human form. She was an extraordinary person. Her kindness and patience with my daughter was incredible. Each time Elizabeth rode, Paula would be on one side of the horse, a volunteer on the opposite side, and another volunteer guided the horse. All the volunteers had hearts of gold. No matter what type of day Elizabeth was having, Paula and the volunteers would brighten it.

Elizabeth loved horses and looked forward to her weekly hippotherapy. Not long into the program, her outpatient occupational therapist, Carla, asked me, "What are you doing differently in Elizabeth's life?" I explained that Elizabeth was doing hippotherapy. Carla said, "I'm seeing such positive changes in your daughter. That's absolutely from hippotherapy."

I was incredibly amazed by Carla's humility. She was also instrumental in Elizabeth's achievements but still gave credit where it must have been due. Elizabeth's new kind of therapy made such a huge difference. Carla observed that Elizabeth would voluntarily use her right side; it wasn't a struggle. She said if Elizabeth didn't have that trauma on the right side of her body, she would have been right-handed.

We continued for four years with weekly hippotherapy sessions. It was truly remarkable. My other two girls loved being on the farm. There was a little playground where the girls would play. They would visit the potbelly pigs, the mini horses, the full-sized horses, and the goats. They also enjoyed playing with the dogs and the chickens that roamed freely on the grounds.

Speech Therapy

Elizabeth was open to working with many different speech therapists. One of her therapists had her name, so she nicknamed her Same Name Elizabeth! Each session challenged her. She would get frustrated because she couldn't hear some of the high-pitched sounds. It was tough for her to pronounce the letters she couldn't hear.

The therapists would give Elizabeth tools to make the sounds of the letters she couldn't hear. Her pronunciation came a long way with the help of her sessions.

Chemotherapy

Elizabeth's first surgery left her with Bell's Palsy in her face, and she could not walk or crawl. She instantly tried crawling when we got home from the hospital. She got mad when she couldn't crawl anymore. It was heartbreaking to see her struggle.

We wanted to give our daughter some fun before she started chemotherapy. Elizabeth was still recovering from surgery, so we needed to consider that. We took her on a carousel ride at our local zoo. Elizabeth loved it. Her Bell's Palsy didn't bother her. She was able to be as joyful as all the other kids on the carousel.

On August 2, 2006, Elizabeth was admitted into HUMC. Her chemotherapy was highly toxic, so she was required to stay in the hospital as they administered it. HUMC had a new Children's Hospital, so each child had their own room. The patients got to choose each meal from the menu HUMC offered. She gobbled up that first dinner, so we were encouraged that she'd do well with the hospital meals.

The following day Elizabeth received her first cocktail of chemotherapy drugs. We had put her in a pretty dress but soon switched to hospital gowns. She needed too many outfit changes from getting sick from the chemo. Elizabeth needed to have a urinary catheter due to the toxicity of the chemo drugs. She didn't like that catheter at all. Things were never going to be the same.

Early every morning, the doctors and their medical team would do the rounds. They would visit each child on the HEM/ONCO floor. Elizabeth would be frightened when this large group of people came into the room. Thankfully, I was still breastfeeding her. Each time the medical team came in, Elizabeth would latch on. Breastfeeding was a huge comfort to her. Before her cancer diagnosis, she had been starting to wean. After her cancer diagnosis, she went from breastfeeding three times to ten times a day. That was a lot, but I didn't mind. It was a blessing to comfort her in the rollercoaster of emotions we were going through. This connection also brought me comfort.

I appreciated the medical team's advice about cutting her hair short. Her hair didn't fall out immediately, but when it did, it came out in clumps. The surprising part was when she lost her eyebrows. It wasn't an area in which I was expecting her to lose her hair. It shocked me.

About a week later, Elizabeth came home from the hospital. We were scared to have her home. We weren't sure we could appropriately care for her. She was a fourteen-month-old cancer patient with tubes coming out of her chest and a body full of chemo. We had considered hiring a nurse to help us at home. Instead, my sister agreed to come and help. It was great to have my sister with us.

For this first round of chemo, Elizabeth had a Medcomp. The Medcomp was a central line with external tubing coming out of her chest, where they administered her chemo. The tubes were heavy and pulled at Elizabeth's skin. We were worried that she might try to tug on them overnight, so she slept in my bed. My sister would come into the bedroom in the middle of the night to give Elizabeth her overnight gastronomy (G-tube) feedings. Elizabeth was given a G-tube because she lost too much weight during her chemo treatments.

Elizabeth's nausea was the worst during her treatment at the hospital, but some sickness would linger on at home. We gave her Zofran for her nausea. When that wasn't enough, we would also give her Ativan. Our house was now like a pharmacy.

Harvest

Between the first and second cycles of chemo, the doctor needed to harvest stem cells from Elizabeth. She had a Medcomp catheter for this reason. The catheter was quite large to allow the stem cell harvest, but it was taking a toll on Elizabeth's small body. We looked forward to the day when she no longer needed it. We brought Elizabeth to HUMC to have the procedure done.

We carried Elizabeth into a room. There were big chairs next to the centrifuges. The doctor needed to take Elizabeth's blood, spin out the stem cells, then return her blood to her. The process had started okay but quickly changed. Elizabeth started getting pale. Then she began throwing up. It was so awful to witness. Even though she was ill, they needed to continue. She was sick a few more times before they finished. The procedure emotionally drained me. Thankfully I was able to take Elizabeth home to recover.

After the stem cell harvest, Elizabeth went in for another catheter surgery. This time they removed the Medcomp catheter and replaced it with a Broviac catheter.

Thankfully the Broviac, though still external, had smaller tubing. The new tubing didn't tug as much on Elizabeth's skin, so it was less worrisome. Even so, we were nervous that Elizabeth could pull the tubes out during the night. We decided to continue to allow her to sleep in my bed.

Hearing Tests

Elizabeth had a baseline hearing test before her chemotherapy started. Every two months, Elizabeth would have to get her hearing tested again. Some of the chemotherapy was ototoxic. The doctors needed to test her hearing often to make sure her hearing wasn't getting worse over time. Based on Elizabeth's cancer protocol, Head Start III, it required hearing tests every two months.

Unfortunately, a child was only allowed one hearing test per year based on our insurance. The hospital tried to bill our insurance for each additional hearing test, but the insurance denied the bills. The medical bills were piling up. I tried to call insurance. A family friend helped draft letters on our behalf to appeal the insurance claims. Unfortunately, nothing worked. We had to negotiate with the hospital to lower the amounts due. We paid a decent sum of money for all the extra hearing tests.

VOD

A few months into Elizabeth's first battle, she developed VOD (veno-occlusive disease). VOD occurred when the liver wasn't working correctly. Instead of the blood getting cleaned through the liver, her liver returned the dirty blood to the body. This was dangerous for Elizabeth.

The doctor arranged to have a particular drug flown in from California to treat her VOD. We had to make sure we were going to get it flown in before it was too late to save our daughter.

The doctor said that typically VOD didn't happen at this phase of the cancer journey; it mostly happened during the stem cell transplant.

Elizabeth had to get daily ultrasounds to see the status of the VOD. It was a scary bunch of days. I would go with Elizabeth and the patient transporter to the ultrasound. I would be tense with anxiety while I waited for the ultrasound tech to give us the preliminary report.

The inpatient doctor said Elizabeth could die from VOD. That didn't sit well with us. We were already dealing with many things that she could die from, so to hear that she could die from this condition pushed us over the edge.

That doctor didn't realize our preference: we didn't want to know the statistics of whether she would live or die; we just wanted to be constantly trying to find the cure. We were well aware that our daughter's prognosis wasn't good.

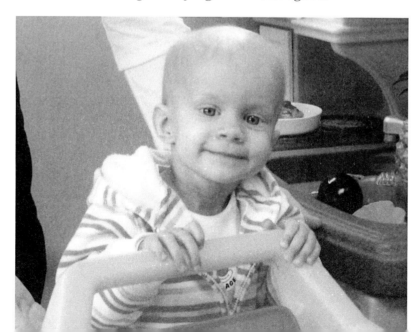

Until then, even though she had cancer, no one talked about the idea that she could die. We always focused on the idea that we might be able to find the solution; that was our goal. So, when that doctor said she could die from VOD, he wasn't even aware of how traumatic it was for us.

The following week, the doctor apologized. He said he hadn't realized how we felt. We appreciated the doctor apologizing. We had yet to have a doctor do this for us. Such a simple act made a huge difference. I hoped this happened more in the future.

Thankfully, Elizabeth never needed that drug. Her liver just naturally started figuring out how to operate normally again.

Breastfeeding

Elizabeth continued to breastfeed frequently through these months of high-dose chemotherapy. The nurses constantly monitored Elizabeth's weight, growth, hearing, and much more due to the toxicity of the chemotherapies. A few months into her treatments, a medical staff member came into the hospital room to say Elizabeth was losing too much weight. She said that my breastmilk was interfering with Elizabeth getting enough nutrients. She told me I needed to stop breastfeeding her.

I was distraught. I knew how much breastfeeding was helping Elizabeth, and I wasn't about to stop! As soon as the nursing staff saw my reaction, they called in the social worker. After the social worker heard how I felt, she contacted the medical staff member to resolve the situation. Thankfully we came to a compromise. I decreased Elizabeth's breastfeeding times, and the medical staff member increased her formula feeds.

Massive Chemotherapy and Stem Cell Transplant

The last month of Head Start III was the worst. The medical staff suggested we wait for her last treatment until after the Christmas and New Year's week. We didn't want to wait. Elizabeth's cancer wouldn't take the week off, so why should we?

Elizabeth arrived on December 26, 2006 to begin treatment. The days leading to her stem cell transplant were counted as negative numbers until day zero, her transplant day. Elizabeth had an entire year's worth of chemo that week. There was a good reason for it because the doctors were trying to completely knock out her immune system. Once the immune system was shut down, her body was ready for the stem cell transplant. They managed somehow to get all that chemo into her poor little body.

On day zero, she received her stem cells. We were hoping and praying that the stem cells would grow as fast as possible so she could have a functioning immune system again.

Each day without an immune system meant every kind of virus, bacteria, or fungus could be her demise. It was the scariest time for us. Her prior chemotherapy treatments had lowered her immune system, but never for this long or with such intensity.

Unfortunately, Elizabeth couldn't keep any of her formula feeds down. Doctors realized what was going on, so they withheld all formula feeds. They said she could only have breastmilk.

Wow! Breastfeeding saved the day during her stem cell transplant! What a difference from a few months earlier. Finally, the medical staff saw the importance of breastfeeding. It was empowering to know that Elizabeth could only have breastmilk during this critical time in her cancer journey. She never got sick from nursing. Now she could start recovering without the trauma of throwing up and she would have the added emotional support benefits too!

During this post-transplant time, it was a very sterile environment. Gowns and masks had to be worn by all medical staff and visitors. We had to wash our hands all the time. There was hand sanitizer, but it wasn't sterile enough. Only a thorough handwashing kept Elizabeth safe.

We were in the hospital on New Year's Eve. We decided to have a New Year's Eve party in the hospital room with Elizabeth. Very few pediatric cancer patients were on the HEM/ONCO floor. The handful of families decided that we would all celebrate together. We ordered some food to share in the family kitchenette area. Another family brought sparkling cider and champagne glasses. It was nice to connect with the other families. We were blessed never to be inpatient again during another holiday.

The Fever

One of the first nights after the stem cell transplant, Elizabeth's fever went above 105 degrees Fahrenheit. That was not good! The entire nursing staff rushed into the room with bags of ice. They put them all over Elizabeth's body. They needed to cool her body down to avoid permanent brain damage. Thankfully the fever did go down, but it wasn't a smooth road. The fever fluctuated up and down, but never got that high again. It was terrifying. If that fever hadn't gone down, she could have died.

Elizabeth was discharged almost a month after the stem cell transplant. It took that long to get her immune system strong enough so she could leave the hospital. We kept her at home except for doctor and therapy appointments. Elizabeth always wore a mask. She managed fine with it.

In 2006, it wasn't usual for people to wear masks. Strangers would ask, "What's wrong with her?" It was frustrating and felt invasive. She needed the extra protection from the mask since her immune system wasn't fully recovered yet. It was none of their business why Elizabeth needed a mask.

Corporate Leave

Elizabeth's condition was critical. My corporate job granted me family leave to take care of her. My job allowed me an indefinite amount of time to care for Elizabeth during her cancer battle. Not only did they give me time off, they also kept paying my salary and benefits. The family leave ensured a continuum of income and fantastic benefits for my family and me, as well as the time I needed to care for my daughter. It was a blessing to have a job that supported me during this rough time!

Elizabeth and Church

We were in church one Sunday when we saw a friend sitting behind us. She was praying the rosary during mass. She asked Elizabeth, "Today, I have three rosaries with me. I want to give you one. Which one would you like?"

Elizabeth picked the purple one. Purple was her favorite color then. She picked up the purple rosary and held the cross upside down.

She then posed a question to her dad and me, "Do you know what this is?"

We said, "No, what?" and she replied, "It's a key to a door."

Wow, it was very profound for a small child to have this insight.

There were other incredible moments during our Sunday masses.

One time we were attending mass at the Jersey Shore. During the service, I was holding the missal and following along. Elizabeth saw how I was holding the missal and said, "No." She took another missal to show me. She closed it and held it over her head. There was a cross on the front cover, and she made sure to have it facing out.

She said, "This is how you hold it." She mimicked what the priest was doing on the altar.

That very same day, she begged me to visit the Virgin Mary. There was a Virgin Mary statue to the left of the altar. Of course, I allowed Elizabeth to see the Virgin Mary statue. After church, she was so happy to spend time with the Virgin Mary. She had a private conversation with her.

We would visit the Virgin Mary statue every Sunday at our home church. She would spend a few minutes with the Virgin Mary before we left the church grounds. Seeing the Virgin Mary was really important to her.

On a different Sunday during mass, Elizabeth pointed to the altar and said, "Mommy, it's Jesus!"

I said, "Where, where?"

She said, "Over there behind the poinsettias!" but I couldn't see him.

I asked Elizabeth, "What does Jesus look like?" but that was it. She was finished talking about it.

When we received communion during mass, she would see us and ask, "When is it my turn?" She was still just a young child, so it was going to be a few years before she could have communion. I didn't have a good answer for her, so I let the question pass without answering. My lack of an answer didn't deter her. She would ask yet again, "When is it my turn?"

She liked to play church with her family and friends. She would give out communion to everyone. She even included the offering at the end of her mass. She went around with a basket and collected money from everyone. She was in her glory!

Therapy Dogs and Animals

When Elizabeth was having inpatient chemotherapy, therapy dogs were a great help to her. The therapy dogs that came to visit her were tiny little dachshunds. They would jump up on her hospital bed to snuggle next to her. Elizabeth would smile from ear to ear. Her therapy dog visits were crucial since she missed her dog, Rudy. He was our golden retriever, always full of love and cuddles. Thankfully these little dogs brought her some comfort and joy during those hospital stays.

Her relationships with different animals were instrumental in helping her. After her first surgery, she was paralyzed on the right side of her body. Only a small amount of function had returned to her right side when she got back from the hospital, so she was reluctant to use it. With the help of a bunny, she was willing to use her compromised right hand to pet it.

Rudy was significant in helping her. He was her everything. He supported her emotionally and physically. She'd always shower Rudy with affection, and Rudy would pay it back tenfold. Rudy knew when to be more playful and when to stay still. It's incredible how dogs know what their humans need!

We were lucky that her physical therapist, Sarah, sometimes brought in her dog to help with Elizabeth's sessions. Part of the therapy was throwing the ball to the dog. Then, the dog retrieved it and brought it back. Elizabeth was thrilled! She willingly threw it again and again. These were some of Elizabeth's favorite sessions.

Her hippotherapy was a highlight of her week. Thanks to those sessions, she progressed faster with her fine motor skills. As a bonus, she got to be on a farm enjoying horses and other animals.

One of her doctors owned a horse. Elizabeth was fortunate enough to be invited to ride the doctor's horse. She went a bunch of times. It was lots of fun for her because Elizabeth was able to ride and feed the horse. She learned that she had to hold her hand flat when the horse took that last piece of carrot. We didn't want the horse to think one of her fingers was an extra piece of carrot!

Remission

After the stem cell transplant, Elizabeth went into remission. A few months into her remission, my sister asked her to be a flower girl at her wedding. Elizabeth's hair was growing back, and it now looked like she had a crew cut. She wore a light purple dress and tiny white shoes. She brought a sense of magic and joy wherever she went. What a gift it was to see her shine at the wedding! She was a pretty princess, with her short hair, her dazzling smile, and her gracefulness.

We had stopped her music classes when she was battling cancer. Now that her treatments were done, I signed her up again. I was expecting the same warm, fuzzy feelings that Elizabeth and I experienced before her diagnosis. I didn't realize that my perspective had changed. We did one set of classes, but things were different. Our reality had changed. I couldn't relate to the other families that were in the class. We also didn't get the same magical feelings we got before treatment. We chose not to continue.

We found other things to do with Elizabeth. New activities were easier than things we had done before her treatments. It helped to be around those that had traveled with us on our journey. It also helped to be around families that had children battling cancer. We were blessed to have cancer support groups and events where we met other cancer families.

For Elizabeth's second birthday, we decided to have a huge celebration. A friend of ours made a castle birthday cake. Nana let us use her backyard. There was a petting zoo, clowns, and pony rides. We were so grateful to have our daughter make it through her grueling cancer treatments. She was alive and well. It was a joy to have this party and show our gratitude!

Mass

Every July twelfth, the anniversary of Elizabeth's diagnosis, we held a mass to celebrate. The celebration honored the fact that Elizabeth survived another year with a stage 4 brain tumor. We knew that each day was precious with Elizabeth, and we were grateful.

We would gather about thirty people together for the celebration. We had a priest come to say a mass. After the service, we would have a big dinner to continue the celebration.

On Elizabeth's fourth anniversary of her diagnosis, like usual, we did the mass and dinner. The priest was able to stay and have dinner with us. We were all chatting over drinks. The priest said that he thought I was pregnant. He said I was glowing. I was surprised. I hadn't even missed a period yet. I took a pregnancy test, and it was positive! It was incredible that the priest was able to tell I was pregnant before I even knew!

Pizza Parties

After every MRI, we would celebrate. No matter whether the news was good or bad, we would head to a pizzeria with friends and family. Elizabeth loved to see everyone. She always wanted to know who was able to come. She would jump up on someone's lap to share her love and infectious laughs.

Elizabeth always lit up the room. When she would see someone she knew, she would run into their arms with a huge hug. Elizabeth had an endless pool of love to give others.

She would shower the hospital workers, classmates, teachers, principal, school nurse, and others with love. Many of her classmates have reflected on their relationship with Elizabeth. A lot of them recall being her best friend. Elizabeth was a great role model. She didn't hold back her love. She never held grudges. She was a happy child. We can all learn from her.

Anger

What does a parent do with anger? I have spent much of my life simply ignoring my anger. Elizabeth's cancer battle brought a lot of frustration to the surface. There were many layers to it. Even though anger would surface, I would do my best to push it down inside me, pretending it didn't exist.

On July 12, 2006, I was distraught with grief, which I understood. What I didn't understand and wasn't willing to recognize was the anger. I fooled myself over the years that I wasn't angry. Why? I wondered. Maybe because of the societal pressure or my genetic makeup. Either way, it wasn't healthy to shove my anger to the deepest, darkest places inside me. My anger had festered inside me for a long time. I'm only now discovering and unwinding it.

I started noticing that simple things could make me extremely angry. I realized that my anger didn't match the situation. I now take the time to work through my angry moments. I use a lot of self-care to help facilitate this process.

Some self-care strategies that have helped are Seimei, meditation, long baths, therapy, walks, hikes, and naps. The idea of taking naps was hardest for me because I saw them as too self-indulgent. I have learned to overcome that. I have needed to rest when the worst of my anger and other strong emotions have come forward. By listening to what my body needs, I've moved more quickly through my healing process. I am no longer having intense anger when small issues occur. I am grateful.

CHAPTER THREE

Camp

Soon after Elizabeth's diagnosis, the vice president of my corporate tax department, reached out to me. He said his daughter was a volunteer at an amazing camp and that she highly recommended it for our family. The camp was for children with life-threatening illnesses. Since Elizabeth was in the middle of a challenging cancer protocol, I took note of it. It just wasn't feasible for Elizabeth to go anywhere at that time.

A few months later on a Saturday, the covering social worker offered his support.

We explained to him that we wanted to give our daughter some fun experiences. We wanted to look at camp possibilities, but we knew her young age would exclude her from a lot of them. He spent his entire Saturday researching this for us. At the end of his shift, he gave us a folder full of camp options! We were thrilled!

His effort that day impacted me so much that I always kept it in the back of my mind. We were too far into cancer treatments to consider camp then, but we now knew there were options for the future. We started thinking about camps again when Elizabeth went into remission in January 2007.

By June 2007, Elizabeth had turned two years old and we applied for a fall camp. We were surprised when the camp said they had an opening in July. They asked if we'd like to come.

One week later, we were going! The camp sessions were about a week long, and the whole family was able to come. It was the first time we got away during Elizabeth's illness. There were children's and parents' activities in the mornings and again in the afternoons. The kids were taken care of by lots of volunteers. I didn't worry for a moment. It was a godsend to have this. I never thought there would be any reprieve during my journey with Elizabeth.

I was grateful for the break, I trusted the wonderful volunteers and staff. It was incredible how the social worker held the space for the large support groups. She ensured everyone got a chance to talk.

These were the biggest support groups I had ever seen. Only a handful of people attended support groups back home. At camp, there were forty to sixty people in the room. The sessions were very emotional, but letting those emotions out was cathartic. It was an excellent healing process but an exhausting one. It would take me a week to have the emotions settle down again.

The first time I was sitting in one of the camp support groups. I had to tell my daughter's story. I felt guilty because my daughter was in remission. Several people around the room had children actively battling cancer and others had endured multiple cancer battles with their children. Elizabeth was the lucky one.

I worried about what the other families would think since my daughter was in remission. Thankfully, the other parents were very welcoming and supportive.

The camp volunteers were fantastic. They treated every child, whether a child with cancer or their sibling, with the same love and kindness. Equal treatment among all the children at camp is vital. At home, the sick child gets much more attention than their siblings. The unequal attention takes a toll on the siblings. It is never the intention to have this happen, but the child with cancer gets more attention due to their diagnosis. That child is brought to many more doctor appointments, hospital visits, therapies, etc., while their siblings stayed with others or came along.

Thankfully at camp, they offered separate support groups for the sick children and their siblings. This way, the cancer children can express themselves to others that understand what they are going through. The same goes for the sibling support group. The camp social worker also invited a few teenage siblings into the parent support group. It helped us to understand their perspective better. Even in the darkest moments, there was light. Camp helped supply the light as well as the supportive community we so desperately needed.

Camp had super-duper blooper games, where they had us do the goofiest things. The games were one of my favorite things at camp. It provided the parents and teens with lots of fun without any sadness. I laughed so hard at the silly things we did, like holding hands in a circle as each of us tried to put our whole body through a hula hoop! The fastest group to go around the circle won the challenge.

Another challenge was balancing an egg on a spoon as you raced across the room and back. If you dropped it on the way, you had to start at the beginning again. There also was the shoe tower challenge. It was always good to have someone who had been at camp before because they would come prepared. There were no guarantees on which challenges would be at that camp session but it was never bad to have a heads up on what might happen! These were the type of ice breakers activities that allowed the space for the deep work you did in the support groups.

The adult and teen teams compete against each other to try to win a trophy. They go head-to-head in challenges. The parents of the teens were most concerned about winning. There were bragging rights for the winning team, making it a tricky ride home if the losing parent or teen were traveling in the same car. There were brain teaser challenges as well as a required performance on stage. Camp gives the teams about thirty minutes to develop a song, a dance, and a team crest.

With such a short time to create a song, a dance, and a crest, the results were not perfect, but it was so much fun! You need to be able to laugh on this journey.

There was a talent show for children and adults, but mostly it was the children that performed. There were children that had varying talents, but no matter what, they got applauded as though they were the best rock stars on the planet. Standing ovations were a regular occurrence. It didn't matter what they did—the violin, gymnastics, sing, and more, the reaction of the audience was the same. It's just remarkable the magic that camp creates! It's been such a blessing in our lives!

We loved attending camp. Most years, we got to go a few times. Camp was a place where everyone was accepted, no matter what. We all understood each other—moms would gather with other moms, and dads would gather with other dads. Families from the same hospital would meet for the first time and bond over similar doctors, nurses, and the like. The diagnosed children understood they weren't the only ones going through this. The siblings connected with other siblings. We all were comforted to know that our feelings were normal and shared by others.

The camp was like Disney World for my girls. They always wanted to know when they could come back. When my children were young, they would be upset as we left camp. We were fortunate because the camp allowed families to come back each year.

Fundraising for Camp

Our family and friends participated in a fundraiser walk in Central Park when she was four. Camp offered donors to purchase a jack-o'-lantern which could be named in honor or memory of someone. Many people donated in this way. Volunteers carved the pumpkins on behalf of the donors.

Camp made a magnificent display of jack-o'-lanterns. Volunteers built an entire structure to hold all the glowing jack-o'-lanterns. There were rows and rows of them. It was enchanting to walk past them in the dark.

The main spot for the walk had a band shell. We were close by when a spokesperson from camp was on the stage. They invited Elizabeth up with them. I went with Elizabeth on stage. She loved it!

Once we were on stage, she started dancing. Next, the camp spokesperson asked if we would represent the camp on the local news. We agreed. They put us in a car and took us to a TV studio. We were like superstars. The TV studio had a green room where they did our hair and makeup as we waited for our interview.

The local news channel interviewed us together with a camp mascot and a few other people. It was brief but so exciting! It was such an honor that camp asked us to represent them for their NYC walk.

That was our best fundraising event for camp. We collected donations ourselves, and others also collected to help our team. It was touching to see the individuals' efforts to fundraise for camp.

Another camp fundraiser was a polar plunge. There were many locations for this event. We went to the one that was closest to us in New Jersey. It was so cold!

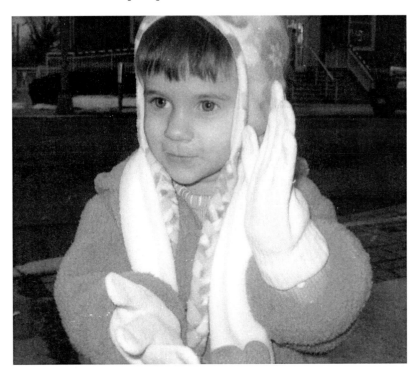

For this event, you would get sponsored to jump into the ice-cold ocean or lake. You did either the chicken dip or the full plunge. My sister and I signed up. She did the full plunge in just a bathing suit! I did the chicken dip fully clothed. At the last minute, Elizabeth decided to join in. She did the chicken dip with me! Even with our clothes and jackets on, we froze as soon as our bare feet hit the cold sand. It only got worse when we went into the water. Thank goodness that we were able to warm up inside afterward!

It was a lot of fun supporting camp in these ways. We've done that for many years. We want to ensure that camp can keep doing its fantastic work.

CHAPTER FOUR

The Second Battle

In August 2007, Elizabeth was once again diagnosed with cancer—the second time this dreaded disease had presented in her life. We were all shocked. She'd just had a seven-month remission.

We were given the gift of a few days before starting medical intervention again. We dropped what we were doing and headed down to Ocean City, Maryland. It was amazing to be at the beach. The ocean waves had such a calming effect on me.

While we were there, we took a day trip to Chincoteague, Virginia, to see the wild ponies. Elizabeth loved horses! We drove through the Assateague Island National Seashore and saw wild ponies in nature. We grabbed a meal before heading back. I got soft-shelled crabs. The other adults thought it was too risky for me to eat them since it was the end of the season. We were also the only ones at the restaurant. Thankfully, I was fine, but one of the other adults did end up with an upset stomach. The end of the season must not have been the best time to eat at that restaurant.

When we got back from the weekend, a friend asked me if I would be open to taking Elizabeth to a healing service at her mom's church. I always accepted healing and prayers as long as the person had good intentions. My friend mentioned that she would have told me sooner but feared that I might have said no since the healing service would be in Spanish. That didn't bother me at all.

We headed into Queens to my friend's mom's church. We went to the healing service. A large group of people made a circle in the narthex of the church to pray for Elizabeth. Next, we went to a little chapel. There was more praying and also a sermon during the service.

It was a very impactful experience. On the way home, my two-year-old put together a couple of words. She hadn't put many words together yet. Her speech had been delayed from all the trauma to her brain.

The words that she put together were "All gone." Elizabeth's dad and I were excited about this. Right after her healing service, our daughter said all gone! Could this mean the healing service cured her cancer? We certainly hoped it was true.

New Plan for Chemotherapy

We were in no man's land now. The first protocol for Elizabeth's cancer had failed, and it was the only known treatment for her type of cancer. Elizabeth's doctor reached out to another pediatric neuro-oncologist in California to bounce off some ideas for the next best steps.

Together, the two doctors decided on a specific combo of chemotherapy drugs. Elizabeth started these drugs right away. The nurses administered all her treatments in the outpatient clinic. The drugs were rough on her body but not as extreme as her first protocol.

With brain tumors, doctors always needed to use more than one chemotherapy at a time. The doctors did this because breaking the blood-brain barrier is difficult. Only with multiple chemotherapies at a time could the chemo be effective in battling brain cancer. Therefore, Elizabeth had a few different chemotherapies given to her at the same time throughout all her chemotherapy treatments.

Feeding Therapy

As the months of chemotherapy continued, Elizabeth ate fewer types of food. The chemotherapy changed her taste buds, so the foods became less enjoyable.

Elizabeth was losing weight, and we needed some intervention. There was a renowned feeding therapist at HUMC. We asked Elizabeth's doctor about getting in to see her. The feeding therapist only took the most extreme cases. Elizabeth's doctor presented the case to her, and she accepted Elizabeth as her patient. We were so thankful.

As the feeding sessions began, Elizabeth gave a bit of pushback. She wouldn't eat all the different foods. She asked to go to the bathroom during the session. The first time the therapist allowed it, but not in the following session. Unfortunately, Elizabeth had an accident. It was a bit of hard love, but Elizabeth learned from it. She went to the bathroom before all of her remaining feeding therapy sessions.

The therapist had me bring in foods of a particular color each week. She asked that I bring in many different foods in that specific color. Then she expected Elizabeth to try each one. She didn't have to eat it all, but she did need to try a small bite or two of each new food.

The therapist gave us homework each week. Elizabeth needed to continue eating the new foods the therapist introduced. We documented Elizabeth's daily progress. We brought the food journal back to the therapist weekly so she could evaluate it.

Luckily, Elizabeth became more willing to try the foods for the therapist. She started to like more fruits and vegetables. This therapy was incredibly important. The better Elizabeth ate, the stronger her body was to endure her grueling treatments.

Pediatric ENT

Elizabeth developed nosebleeds during her second battle with cancer. We needed to take her to the Pediatric Ears, Nose and Throat (ENT). Nana and I brought Elizabeth for the consultation. The doctor told us that Elizabeth needed a nasal endoscopy. We came back a week later for the procedure.

No one prepared us for the procedure. We were in the exam room waiting for the doctor. The doctor entered the room and asked us to pin Elizabeth's arms and legs down. I thought, *Huh?* I guess we had no choice. Elizabeth fought us a bit but then resigned to what was going to happen. Pinning her down was a horrible burden to Nana and me. I wish there could have been a more child-friendly approach to the nasal endoscopy.

The doctor abruptly inserted the camera into Elizabeth's nose to do the procedure. The insertion of the camera could have gone better for Elizabeth. The whole experience frightened her.

After the doctor finished the endoscopy, he said the best thing to do would be to stop the chemo. He knew this wasn't a realistic option. Instead, he gave us tips and tools to get the nosebleeds to stop. We followed his advice and it worked, but we never returned to his office.

The experience had been so traumatic to Elizabeth that it took her six months to be able to trust doctors again. She went to the doctor all the time. It was a challenging setback and added a lot of undue stress to her future doctor visits.

I searched for a different Pediatric ENT. I found one further away, but I was okay with the extra drive. We changed doctors. What a good decision!

Contrast

Elizabeth needed to have a CT (computed tomography) scan. The doctor required Elizabeth to drink contrast to get the CT images. I have heard that each time you swallowed contrast, it gets more and more stuck in your throat, making it harder and harder to take each additional sip.

When Elizabeth had to take it, she wanted to stop within the first few sips. She still had most of the contrast left to drink. Nana and I tried to reason with her to drink it, but nothing worked.

Nana remembered how Elizabeth liked the iPads that she got to use at the hospital. Nana told Elizabeth that if she drank all her contrast, she would get an iPad on the way home. Well, that worked. Elizabeth kept drinking the contrast and got through about half of it. Thankfully, the nurse said it was enough contrast to have a successful CT scan. The technician finished the scan, and off we went to the Apple Store. What a lucky little girl! She deserved it.

Third Birthday Party

Some of our close family and friends helped us throw another large birthday party for Elizabeth. This time it was carnival themed. We brought back the petting zoo and pony rides. We added face-in-the-hole boards, carnival games, and more. Most of our guests went home with a pet goldfish!

At the end of Elizabeth's party, she went inside because she wasn't feeling well. She was having poop issues. She had gone about eight times in an hour, and it smelled weird. When we got her to the doctor, they tested her poop and discovered that she had *clostridium difficile*, C. diff. This type of bacterial infection was very challenging. There was also excruciating pain. C. diff causes inflammation in the colon, as well as cramping, and diarrhea. The infectious disease doctors put her on high-dose antibiotics for two months.

She didn't have cramping or diarrhea at the end of the two months. They retested her and she was negative for C. diff. This was great until the chemo treatments dropped her immune system again and the C. diff. was back. I would always know before the test results came back because there was an awful smell.

Doctors always gave her two months' worth of high-dose antibiotics. Since the C. diff kept returning when her immune system dropped, the doctors concluded that she never got rid of it. The infection remained dormant in her body until her immune system dropped again. We found that even though she tested clear, we never could be sure that it wouldn't come back.

Radiation

Elizabeth had MRIs every three months to see if her cancer was stable. On the second MRI of the second battle, her cancer had progressed. Doctors had to quickly scramble for the next new chemotherapies that might put her cancer into remission.

After almost a year of a few different chemotherapy cocktails, the treatments were wearing on her. The doctors said she couldn't get any more chemo because it would be too much for her body. Luckily, we had the option of radiation.

Elizabeth's original protocol, Head Start III, had included radiation. Since she had been only a year old during her first cancer battle, it would have been too risky to give her radiation, especially on a cognitive level. From birth to age three, a child has already gained seventy-five percent of their knowledge for life. The goal from the beginning, if we ever needed it, was to get her to three years old so she could receive full brain and spine radiation as safely as possible.

It was time to start the planning process for radiation. The whole process took a few weeks. The medical staff created a body mold for Elizabeth to ensure she would be in the same position every time she received radiation. She also was given tiny little tattoos on her back. These tattoos guaranteed that the radiation beams were placed in the same exact spot every time. During this planning process, I was eight months pregnant with my second child.

I gave birth to Mary on August 1, 2008. I went into labor naturally, but her heart rate dropped. The doctors gave me time to deliver the baby naturally. It didn't work so I had a c-section. Due to this, I couldn't get out of bed when Elizabeth came to visit me. I had an IV (intravenous) in my arm—or a tubie, as Elizabeth called it. When Elizabeth saw my tubie, she got scared. She wanted to leave immediately. Elizabeth thought I was sick. She left quickly.

By the next day, I requested that the nurse remove my IV. I didn't want to have it in when Elizabeth came to visit. It took a lot of begging and pleading with my nurse, but I got it out right before Elizabeth came. This visit was so much better. Elizabeth wasn't scared. To her, Mommy wasn't sick anymore. She stayed longer and got to hold her baby sister.

I was eager to get home. I negotiated with my doctor to discharge me after three days rather than four, which was the standard for a c-section. It was good to be home, but climbing the stairs was difficult. Thankfully I recovered quickly.

Two weeks later, Elizabeth started her radiation treatments. On the first day of her treatments, baby Mary didn't come along. Elizabeth was nervous, but she got through it.

The treatments were five days a week, for six weeks in a row. On the second day, we brought her sister Mary. Elizabeth became nervous when she got into the exam room. She said, "Mommy, I want to hold my baby sister."

I said, "Oh, okay," and I put her baby sister in her arms. A peace came over her. It was beautiful. I thought, *Oh my gosh, I should have had a second baby sooner.*

Who would have ever known that her baby sister would make such a big difference? Baby Mary was able to bring her big sister such peace. Mary truly helped Elizabeth to get through all her radiation without such angst.

Thankfully Elizabeth never got burned by the radiation, but she was now completely bald. The radiation had caused her hair to fall out.

After a few months, she did get some of her hair back. A patch of hair on the back of her head never returned, but it didn't faze her. She never wanted a wig. She was such a strong and incredibly resilient three-year-old.

She went into remission after she finished radiation. One of the side effects from her treatments was that the growth of her spine was stunted forever. Her torso would stay the same size for the rest of her life.

Second Corporate Leave

My corporate job was very generous during her second battle with cancer. They granted me another medical family leave and continued paying my salary and benefits. It was a huge blessing, especially to have insurance benefits while Elizabeth was fighting cancer. This battle was much longer, so eventually, the corporation changed my leave status to maternity leave.

I had gotten pregnant early into Elizabeth's second battle. Before I got pregnant, I wanted to rule out that Elizabeth's cancer was not because of a predisposition for cancer in our family genes.

Thankfully doctors tested Elizabeth and gave us a ninety-six percent certainty that Elizabeth's cancer had nothing to do with her genes. They said that all families have a 1 in 10,000 chance of having a child with cancer. The doctors gave us the confidence to proceed with another pregnancy without worrying about cancer.

Once Mary was born, I had eight weeks of short-term disability and three months of family leave. The return date of my maternity leave ended up being different than what I had thought. Human Resources called me a few days before their calculated return date and said I would lose my job if I didn't return that Friday. My calculation was a week after theirs. That Friday, I needed to be at the hospital for one of Elizabeth's outpatient visits. Elizabeth was still very fragile. She would need more rehabilitation before I would be ready to return to work. I chose my daughter over my job so my corporate job ended.

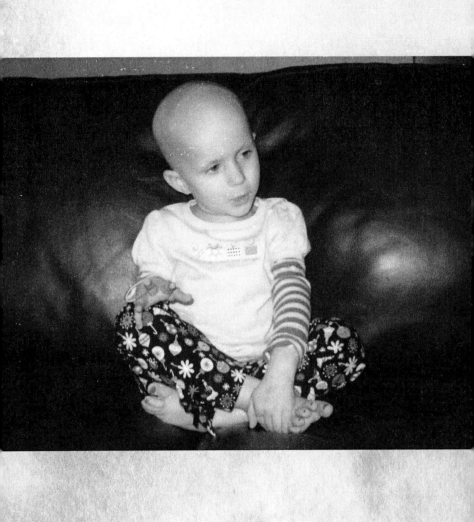

CHAPTER FIVE

The Big Remission

During Elizabeth's last year of preschool and her first year of elementary school, she had two full years of remission. She was at the same preschool from three to five years old. It was beautiful to have the school and community supporting us. They had seen Elizabeth finish her radiation treatments at three years old. They also saw her get stronger and healthier during her remission.

Elizabeth had the chance to graduate from preschool. She got to wear a graduation cap with a pretty dress. Elizabeth was in the front row and proudly walked up to receive her diploma. She celebrated with her classmates in the schoolyard after the ceremony. Later that night, we celebrated Elizabeth's graduation with the extended family. We were so excited to have this special moment with her.

For kindergarten, she was in a small classroom. There were students from kindergarten to second grade (K-2) in class with her. She had excellent teachers, aides, therapists, and classmates. They all supported Elizabeth.

It was great that Elizabeth had older kids in her class. The boys were like big brothers to her. They looked out for her.

All of the teachers and staff adored Elizabeth. Elizabeth brought out the best in the people around her.

Elizabeth had a one-on-one aide in her general and special education classrooms. Her aide matched up perfectly with her! She would always be there for whatever Elizabeth needed. My daughter developed quite a bond with her.

Elizabeth was a talented artist. She could draw quite detailed scenes at a very young age. She really enjoyed going to art class. It was amazing to see the scenes she created.

Elizabeth loved going to school. As she got older, she realized that kids her age didn't go to the doctor and hospital as much as she did. She preferred being in class rather than going to medical appointments. Unfortunately, we didn't have a choice about bringing her so she managed as best she could.

Summer Recreation Camp

Elizabeth attended a summer recreation program in our town while she was in remission. She enjoyed going there, and the staff were very accommodating. She just adored everyone there.

If a day was scorching or Elizabeth felt too tired, the camp counselors would allow Elizabeth to do indoor activities. We were blessed to live in a community that supported our unique situation with Elizabeth. I appreciated that the staff was aware of this and made some extra allowances for her. The changes made by the camp counselors allowed Elizabeth to still partake in camp with the daily fun themes as well as play with her friends.

Disney World

When Elizabeth was five years old and Mary was two, we went to Disney World. Elizabeth wanted to meet Mickey Mouse. We waited in a long line but finally got there. We were lucky to see both Mickey and Minnie Mouse! Elizabeth gave both of them big hugs. She was amazed to meet them in person! Oh, the joys of childhood!

Elizabeth and Mary rode the carousel, Aladdin's carpet ride, It's a Small World, and other rides. They also went to the Monster's Inc. Laugh Floor, where they picked Elizabeth out of the crowd as Boo, the little girl from the movie Monster's Inc. The producers put Elizabeth on a big TV screen in the front of the theater. She loved being in the show!

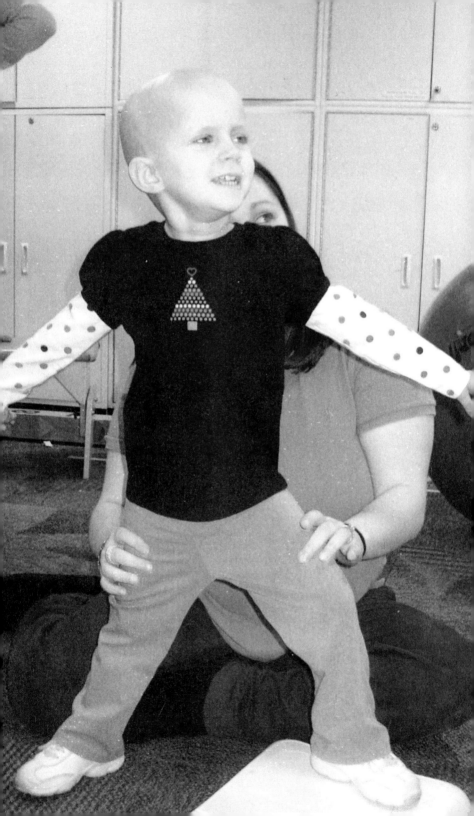

The girls also went to PhilharMagic. It was a long wait. Midway through waiting, Elizabeth had to go to the bathroom! Luckily, I had brought the foldable toilet. It saved the day!

Delivery

I gave birth to my third child, Anna, on March 30, 2011. It was my easiest labor and delivery. I went naturally into labor. Doctors had given me until 1 pm to deliver naturally on March 30; otherwise, they would have done a c-section. I didn't want surgery. Luckily Anna was born a few hours before the 1 pm deadline!

I negotiated with my doctor to let me out of the hospital after one night instead of the usual two nights for natural birth. After all, I needed to get home for my two other children. The doctor approved the early discharge. I didn't have an incision to recover from and it made a huge difference!

Town Pool

Elizabeth, Mary, and Anna loved to go to the pool. They took swimming lessons there. We would meet up with friends and spend summer days playing in the kiddie pool. Some other parents and kids from town would join in and play too. Elizabeth would have belly laughs over the silly things the others would do. Mary would follow her big sister around, enjoying all the shenanigans. Anna would hang out on my lap in and out of the water. Anna was still very young, but she would watch her sisters and smile.

Bergen County Zoo

Elizabeth and her sisters loved going to the zoo. Our local zoo was close by and a good size for young kids. The monkeys were the favorite animal to visit. The barn with the horse, cow, pigs, and owls was a close second. We would venture there during the week when it was less busy.

There was a train ride that went around the entire zoo. We enjoyed riding the train with our friends and family. It was an excellent way to see the zoo without walking around, especially when Elizabeth was exhausted.

There was a carousel ride with lots of different animals to ride on and benches to sit on. Elizabeth and her sisters would choose animals most of the time. When Elizabeth was extra tired, she and I would sit on a bench instead. I was happy that there was a safer solution when she was extra worn out so she didn't have to miss it. Carousels have brought lots of joy to my girls over the years.

Ice Cream

Elizabeth had a favorite ice cream place close by. We went there as a special treat on non-treatment days. Her favorite order was vanilla ice cream with mini gummy bears on top. No matter which ice cream place we went to, she would always get the same thing.

Ice cream has a magical way of bringing joy to most children. Her favorite place continued to be a blessing even during the remission times. We would sit outside on the benches to enjoy the delicious ice cream and the beautiful weather. Each bite of the ice cream helped dissolved more and more of our worries.

First-Year Birthday Celebrations

We've done something for each of my girls to celebrate their monthly birthdays during their first year of life. For the monthly birthday celebration of my youngest daughter Anna, we shared most of them with Elizabeth's best friend's family.

We would have a birthday cake or cupcakes, and we'd always have a dance party. At one of the celebrations, Elizabeth discovered a favorite song. That song is "Love You Like A Love Song" by Selena Gomez.

It brings me joy and sadness when that song comes on the radio. The joy is because I feel so close to her at that moment, and the sadness is because I am more aware of how much I miss her. I still choose to listen to the song every time because the joy far outweighs the sadness.

New Pediatric ENT

We took Elizabeth to the new pediatric ENT for help with her excess ear wax buildup. We sat for a long time in the waiting room, then finally got into the exam room to see the doctor. When the doctor came in, she turned on a noisy machine. Elizabeth got scared. The doctor saw Elizabeth's reaction and immediately shut it off.

The doctor lowered herself to Elizabeth's eye level to speak to her. The doctor told her she had a choice. She said, "Would you like to have the noisy machine or the alligator scissors remove your ear wax? You can take some time to decide what you want to do." The doctor left the room to see another patient.

When the doctor returned, Elizabeth had calmed down. Elizabeth felt empowered because she got to choose what the doctor was going to do. Elizabeth decided to go with the alligator scissors. The procedure was quick and effective. A huge chunk of ear wax came out of Elizabeth's ear! The alligator scissors didn't make a loud sound, so she wasn't frightened. Thank goodness we found a doctor that was so kind!

The doctor said Elizabeth might need ear tubes to help with drainage and hearing. She didn't push us to decide that day; instead, she said she would monitor Elizabeth over time. Not getting pushed into surgery felt good. The prior ENT wanted to do ear tubes right away.

Elizabeth's occupational therapist told us about a chiropractor down the shore that might help with Elizabeth's ears. I was intrigued and decided it was worth the long drive to her office. The office was near Point Pleasant, New Jersey, so we decided to go to the boardwalk after her appointment.

The chiropractor was very kind and welcoming. Elizabeth didn't mind the chiropractic adjustment. The doctor said Elizabeth needed to come back two more times within the week. She said the ear fluid would come out either by Elizabeth throwing up or pooping. She said it would depend on the strength of Elizabeth's stomach.

Just like the chiropractor said, Elizabeth cleared the ear fluid. Her stomach was strong, so the ear fluid exited her body the other way. We were so glad this could happen in such a natural way. Unfortunately, her ears clogged up again. Making weekly drives to see the chiropractor wasn't feasible, so we returned to the pediatric ENT. We decided to go ahead with the ear tube surgery for Elizabeth.

Elizabeth went to a different hospital for her ear tube surgery. It was the hospital where the pediatric ENT was affiliated. We were hopeful this would be the solution for her ears.

Unfortunately, the ear tubes didn't resolve the problem. The doctor deduced that Elizabeth's radiation had left her with scar tissue in her inner ears, which permanently restricted the flow of her ear fluid.

Elizabeth was able to manage with limited hearing due to the fluid buildup. She was such a trouper, not letting this or other things bother her. She always lived in the present moment.

Growth Hormones

Two and a half years after Elizabeth finished her radiation, her pediatric neuro-oncologist informed us that she was cleared for growth hormones. We went to the endocrinologist with Elizabeth and he explained how she would get started.

He told us that two potential types of leukemia could be side effects of the growth hormones. This worried us. Elizabeth had already had other chemotherapies that had the possible side effect of getting leukemia.

I thought to myself, *Oh gosh, I can't start Elizabeth on the growth hormones because it could increase her chances of getting leukemia.* Due to this, I chose to delay it.

The pediatric neuro-oncologist found out the growth hormone therapy was delayed. He explained that if we were going to be worried about side effects, the possibility of getting leukemia shouldn't be our biggest concern.

The bigger concern was that when someone takes growth hormone, it grows *all* the cells in their body. In other words, if Elizabeth had even a single cancer cell left in her body, the cancer cell would grow along with the rest of her regular cells.

In short, the doctor felt that it was worth the risk. We finally decided to move forward with the growth hormone. Two months had past since we had gotten the original clearance to start growth hormone.

The growth hormone was given by way of a shot. It wasn't like a traditional shot, but rather it was an injection pen. I would give Elizabeth the medicine daily.

I took the injection pen and attached a new needle each time. Next, I dialed the dosage amount and then it was ready to give to Elizabeth. I then pushed the button and it injected the right amount of medicine into Elizabeth. She was a real trouper. She took these shots without any complaints.

Her first three-month MRI after starting the growth hormone, in March 2011, went great. She had a clean bill of health.

At this point, we were far enough out from her cancer battle that the doctors moved her MRIs from every three months to every six months. This was the first time since Elizabeth was diagnosed that we had MRIs that far apart. It was exciting, but also scary.

CHAPTER SIX

The Third Diagnosis and Finding Seimei

In September 2011, Elizabeth had her first six-month MRI. It showed that the cancer had come back. This news was extremely crippling. The doctors had ordered a special, more detailed type of MRI in March 2011 known as an MR spectroscopy.

The MR spectroscopy goes into further detail, helping to detect the difference between normal brain tissue and abnormal cancer cells. The results came back that she was cancer free. How could her cancer be back when the MR spectroscopy ruled out cancer just six months before?

Her pediatric neuro-oncologist said to immediately stop the growth hormone. Though we had this bad news of recurring cancer, there was good news too. The growth hormone gave her another four and a half inches of height.

Elizabeth's extra height was all in her legs and arms because the radiation had permanently stunted her spine. This ended up making her limbs longer than usual. Most people didn't notice but our close family did. Her nana would shorten her shirts so that they weren't overly long on her. This helped to make Elizabeth's longer limbs less noticeable. I was grateful for this!

A further discovery from the MRI was that they saw something on Elizabeth's liver and something in her hips. They deduced that cancer had spread to her organs and bones.

This was completely crushing news.

They wanted to confirm these assumptions, so they did an X-ray of her hip. We got some good news. Nothing lit up. It was just a normal void in her hip.

Next, they wanted to see what was going on in the liver. The pediatric surgeon said that he wanted to take sixty percent of her liver out. He said it would regrow, so it wasn't a big deal.

We didn't like that idea so the doctor offered to do something else. A needle biopsy could be done on the tumors in Elizabeth's liver. The only thing was that if she started to bleed out, she would need emergency surgery.

We said we would much rather take the chance of doing a needle biopsy, rather than a sixty percent resection of her liver.

We proceeded with the needle biopsy. Her dad and I would always take turns on who would bring her into a procedure. This time it was her dad who took her in. When he was bringing her into the room, the interventional radiologist said, "I'm here to confirm the metastasis."

Her dad said, "I beg your pardon. We are here to confirm that it's not."

I was very happy that the interaction had happened with her dad. I was in a pretty fragile place, and I probably wouldn't have reacted as politely.

The interventional radiologist performed the biopsy and there was no bleeding. When we got the pathology back, it said there wasn't metastasis. The spots were benign growths that anyone could have on their liver.

You can't unwind the emotional toll you experience when the doctors tell you that your daughter's cancer had spread to her organs and bones. But thankfully you can recover some of the emotional toll when doctors conclude that the cancer did not spread to the organs and bones based on further testing. Now Elizabeth only had to deal with the brain tumor. It was still a big battle but better than what we had originally been told.

Elizabeth had to have a craniotomy. Her two prior craniotomies were when she was one and two years old. By now, she knew that the other kids her age didn't have to do things like this, so she required some type of explanation. I told her that she had something like a bologna sandwich in her head, and it shouldn't be there. It needed to be taken out. She accepted that.

The surgery left her in horrible pain, but thankfully she recovered quickly. Her reaction was very difficult for us to witness. Now at six, she reacted in a much bigger way. Another surgery was needed to place a port in her chest. I hadn't realized how Elizabeth would react. It was a same-day surgery. I had prepared her for the craniotomy but hadn't realized that I should have done the same for the port surgery.

When we got out of the hospital after the port surgery, she felt a bump on her chest. She asked me what it was, and I told her. She started shrieking, "No, Mommy, no! Take this out of me! Take it out now!" Of course, I couldn't. It was just Elizabeth and me in the car. I was driving out of the hospital parking garage when she had this reaction.

I pulled the car over and called the child life therapist. They did their best trying to give me ideas on what I could do to calm her down, but she still was upset. I had no choice but to drive home while she was upset. At home, she was able to calm down. Thankfully she began to accept this new bump on her chest.

Elizabeth had become wise about how the world worked. When she was younger, she probably thought that every young child went to the hospital to have procedures done and to take yucky medicine. She now knew that most kids didn't spend their days at the hospital. Kids didn't go to different specialists, therapies, and procedures all the time.

When she was diagnosed again in first grade, she turned to me and said, "Mommy, I just want to go to school every day." That was her way of saying, "I don't want to do this again." She just wanted to be a normal kid. It broke my heart to hear this. I had wished so hard that there was a way that she didn't have to battle again but there was no choice. We were still determined to find a cure for her cancer.

Having a rare brain tumor come back a third time was devastating news. Her chances of survival were vanishing quickly. In truth, the survival rates had been quite small at the first presentation of the disease and smaller yet at the second presentation. Now with a third presentation, her chances of long-term survival were pretty close to zero.

This made me think that maybe there was something more we could be doing to complement Elizabeth's traditional medicine. Up until this point, friends and family had brought us supplements and different things to try for Elizabeth. We would always go to her doctors and ask if it was okay to use the supplements and tools. Every single time the doctors would say no. Their reasoning was that it might conflict with the chemotherapy.

Finding Seimei

In November 2011, I thought again that there must be something else that we could be doing to help Elizabeth. I was at hippotherapy with Elizabeth and her sisters when I saw another mom and her son. He had just finished his session. I knew the mom from the outpatient therapy center. I remembered that she had been using holistic techniques to help her son recover from a car accident.

I went to her and asked, "What are you doing now to help your son?"

She said, "I do this thing called Seimei."

I said, "I'm interested in knowing more."

She replied, "They are open to the public tonight."

I said, "Okay, I'll see you later tonight."

Later on, I went to the Seimei center. I brought my three daughters with me. Elizabeth was six years old, Mary was three years old, and Anna was seven months old. I walked into the center, and I felt like I was home and that I was being enveloped in love.

During the first five years of Elizabeth's illness, my intuition was non-existent. But as I entered the center, I immediately had these inner knowings. It was incredible. It helped me to feel less nervous to walk in. There was a whole room of people I didn't know and normally that would be a bit overwhelming to me.

I saw that people sat in chairs to receive Seimei, so I had Elizabeth sit in one of the chairs. I asked, "Please, please help my daughter."

The Seimei practitioner said, "Mom, you sit down too."

I said, "No, my daughter needs your help."

The Seimei practitioner said, "No, Mom, you sit down. You're going to get Seimei too."

Elizabeth and I received Seimei sessions as Mary and Anna quietly played. We donated on our way out the door. All the public sessions were by donation at that time. I found out that they were open twice a week, every week. Something in my gut told me that I needed to get there twice a week, every week, and that's exactly what I did.

About three weeks later, when I brought Elizabeth in for her bi-weekly Seimei session a new focus was chosen. The Seimei practitioner said, "Oh, today we're going to help her to walk and run better."

Elizabeth was wearing orthotics on her legs due to a weakness she had from her very first surgery. The surgery had left her hemiplegic, with paralysis of one side of the body. The paralysis had affected her right side. Her brain tumor was on the left side of her brain, which controlled the right side of the body. This was why the right side of her body was affected.

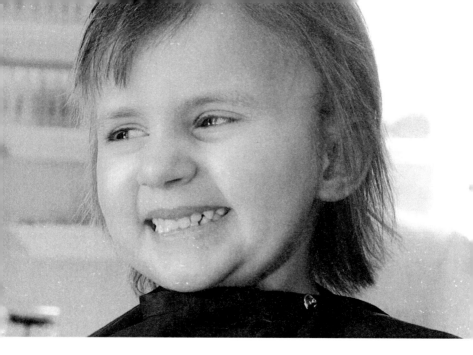

Thankfully, she quickly started getting sensations back on her right side with her therapy sessions. Those physical and occupational therapy sessions allowed her to get back to walking and running, though it wasn't a fluid walk.

When the Seimei practitioners decided to help her with her walking and running, I thought it was a fantastic idea!

After they had worked on her, the Seimei practitioner said, "Okay Elizabeth, go run around the room."

She got up and ran across the room more beautifully than she had ever done in her life. I choked up with tears of joy.

I now knew without a doubt I needed to learn this as quickly as possible! I asked, "Where do I sign up?" Within two months, I got started on my journey to learn Seimei.

Code Blue

In December 2011, Elizabeth had her next MRI. We took her to get her port accessed at the outpatient pediatric oncology clinic. The nurses there had the most experience with accessing children's ports so it was the most comfortable and quickest way for Elizabeth to get it done. Elizabeth knew all the nurses at the clinic, which helped her to be less fearful of the process.

We brought her into one of the outpatient exam rooms. She was accessed quickly. We were waiting for Elizabeth to get her hospital transport to the MRI department. Elizabeth's assigned pediatric oncology nurse that day had worked in the PICU before transferring to the outpatient clinic. We were blessed to have this nurse assigned to Elizabeth that day. She noticed something wasn't right with Elizabeth's vitals. She remained calm and stepped out of the room briefly.

A code blue was called, but we didn't realize it was called for Elizabeth. Elizabeth's heartrate was dropping fast, so the nurse asked for Elizabeth's doctor. The nurse knew the rescue drug that Elizabeth needed and had already gotten it from the pharmacy. She hooked it up and waited for the doctor.

The nurse kept her finger on the slider clamp of the IV tubing as she waited for the doctor to arrive. As soon as the doctor approved the medicine, she released the clamp. Elizabeth instantly began receiving the rescue drug called dopamine. Next, they rushed her up to the PICU.

They found the reason why she was flatlining. She had sepsis, an infection in her body that had traveled to her heart. Once the infection is in your heart, it starts shutting it down.

This was occurring on the very same day that the Seimei center was going to have an open night for the public. I turned to Elizabeth's nana and said, "I know you're going to want to be here with us, but please go to the Seimei center. Tell them what happened to Elizabeth so that they can help her." She left my daughter's bedside to go to the Seimei center, and she relayed the message.

The Seimei center reached out to the head teacher in America. The head teacher said, "No one is to work on Elizabeth but me." For a week straight, she worked on my daughter.

After five days, Elizabeth got out of the PICU and went back to the regular pediatric HEM/ONCO floor. She was out of the hospital two days after that. Within a week, she was fully recovered. Seimei helped her in a huge way.

Through all the times we were at the hospital and even times at home, our friends and family rallied around us. They would bring us food. Sometimes they brought take-out, other times it would be homemade. Whatever the case, it was so appreciated to have the food already prepared and ready for us. We're so very grateful to everyone who helped us with those meals along the way.

Learning Seimei

In January 2012, I did my first-weekend class for level 1 Seimei. It was incredible! After I finished the first day of training, I went to see my parents and sister. I was already able to work on them and make positive changes in their bodies. They were able to feel the changes. What an amazing tool I had within me now!

The Seimei teacher had given me bath salts that had the power of Seimei within them. She said I should take a bath with the salts to help with the sore muscles. I was really happy to have the bath salts. My muscles were sore after a whole day of class. It was amazing to see how the Seimei bath salts melted my soreness away!

It was so empowering for me to have this tool to help my family. There were no supplements or additives needed. During those earlier five years of Elizabeth's illness, before I had Seimei, I would always have this ache in my heart. I would think, *I love her so much. I hug and kiss her all the time. I shower her with love. Why wasn't my love enough to make her cancer go away?*

Now that I had learned Seimei, I felt like I was making a difference. Her journey with cancer would forever be changed.

Spinal Tap

Soon after learning about Seimei, Elizabeth had a spinal tap procedure. It wasn't just a spinal tap though. They took out spinal fluid and replaced it with chemotherapy. The chemo went directly into the cerebrospinal fluid of her brain and spine.

In the past when she had any kind of spinal tap done, she had bad pain at the puncture site. This was the first time I was able to do Seimei to help her recover more quickly from the spinal tap.

The spinal tap was an outpatient procedure. They anesthetized Elizabeth for the procedure. When the procedure was done, they brought her back to an exam room. She was still sleeping when the other members of the family and I were there. I placed one of my hands above her and the other on her side since she was laying down on the gurney. I proceeded to do Seimei for her. The back of my hand changed color for a bit and then went back to normal. I hadn't seen this before. I finished working on Elizabeth before she woke up.

Elizabeth got up soon after I was done. She didn't complain about the puncture wound on her back. I thought, *Wow, this was not how she typically woke from a spinal tap.* She continued to experience no pain from the puncture site while at home.

Elizabeth woke up the next morning and her three-year-old sister Mary asked, "Why do you have a Band-Aid on your back?" Elizabeth shrugged and said, "I don't know." She had no pain whatsoever from the spinal tap. I reflected again on how amazing that was.

It was a huge relief to me to be able to use Seimei to help Elizabeth and others. To have the ability to do that was so empowering, so amazing, so incredible. To finally be making a difference just brought me to tears. Happy tears, of course!

I knew my love was making a difference, but it didn't show in such a huge way as it did when I used Seimei.

Routine Blood Work

One day we were traveling to the hospital because she needed some routine blood work done. She was worked up about it. Thankfully, I had other family members that were driving in the minivan with me, so I was able to get into the back with Elizabeth. I decided that I would do Seimei as we drove to the hospital about twenty minutes away.

During the twenty minute drive, she went from being very anxious to calm and relaxed. Seimei had helped her so she wouldn't be stressed out getting her blood drawn. When she got to the outpatient clinic, she was very cooperative with the nurses. It was a quick process and it went very smoothly.

CHAPTER SEVEN

The Journey Home

In March 2012, Elizabeth got her next MRI. This MRI showed that the disease progressed again. Due to this, we reached out to a doctor from Germany who specialized in her specific type of brain cancer. The doctor had been working at MD Anderson Hospital in Texas when Elizabeth was first diagnosed.

When we researched where he was now, we found out that he was at The Floating Hospital in Massachusetts. He was now close enough to drive there! During this third cancer battle with Elizabeth, it gave us a ray of hope.

When the Seimei community heard about the disease progressing, a collection of practitioners was assembled. Practitioners were assigned to work on Elizabeth each day. Some practitioners offered to work on Elizabeth every day! Three practitioners would work on her daily. Elizabeth would receive a session in the morning, one in the afternoon, and another in the evening. In addition to that, there was a once-weekly practitioner that would also work on Elizabeth.

Thankfully I was a pracitiioner too, so I would work on Elizabeth in between the other sessions. It was such an empowering thing to be able to help my daughter myself! Time and time again, I would turn to Seimei to help with her pain, anxiety, eating habits, and much more. I am forever grateful to have Seimei in my life. It has been nothing short of a lifesaver!

2012 Camp Trips

Later in Elizabeth's cancer battle, she became more fragile. At this time, we were lucky enough to go in February 2012 and March 2012.

On our February 2012 camp trip, Elizabeth got very close with a volunteer named Jenny. She was Elizabeth's one-to-one for that camp session. At camp, kids with one-to-ones had more flexibility in their camp schedule. A lot of the time, Elizabeth wanted to be in the computer lab. She liked to play video games there. The bond between Jenny and Elizabeth continued far past that camp session. We kept in touch, and Jenny came to visit the following year.

In March 2012, camp called me and asked if we wanted to come back. A child with the same diagnosis as Elizabeth was attending camp that week. Until then, we hadn't met anyone with the same diagnosis. At prior camp sessions, I had asked the camp social worker to contact us if there was ever a child with the same diagnosis coming to camp. Thankfully she remembered this. We took the opportunity and went later that week.

Elizabeth immediately bonded with the child that had the same diagnosis. The mother of this child helped me too. I felt guilty about Elizabeth's illness and had created a reason why it might have been my fault. The other mom assured me that she had never done that specific thing when she had been pregnant, and her son had still gotten the same cancer. She told me I had to drop that guilty feeling right away. Her perspective helped me realize that my feelings of guilt were unfounded.

I found out that her son was going to the Floating Hospital. Since he had the same diagnosis as Elizabeth, he was seeing the same specialist. His mom was able to get Elizabeth in quickly so she could get a second opinion. Thank goodness I met them!

That March camp week, we also bonded with another special volunteer that was Elizabeth's assigned one-on-one. She was an occupational therapist, and she helped Elizabeth with her fine motor skills during camp activities. Elizabeth didn't even realize that she was doing therapy. It was perfect! It was so generous of the volunteer to do that for Elizabeth.

Trips to Massachusetts

The first time that we went up to Massachusetts, Elizabeth was in a lot of pain. To make her more comfortable, we let her lie down in the back seat. It was a long drive from New Jersey to Massachusetts. It wasn't an easy ride for her, but the change in positioning helped.

When we got there, she wasn't walking all that well. The long ride had taken a toll on her. We saw the boy from camp and his mom at the hospital. They had an appointment the same day. It helped Elizabeth to see her friend from camp in the waiting room. They both played on Elizabeth's iPad. They took selfies together.

When the doctor saw Elizabeth, he stated that her disease had progressed. He made this determination because he saw she was having a hard time walking. We weren't in that head space yet. We had just taken a long drive to get his opinion on the next best way to treat her cancer.

It was still a good experience to have some guidance from him. He gave some different options to battle her cancer. His preference was to have her be treated at his hospital. Thankfully, he gave us another option to take his recommendations and use them back at HUMC. This made it feasible to proceed, so we went forward with his treatment plan.

We made a second visit to the Floating Hospital a few weeks later. This time Elizabeth was walking and functioning better. It was hard for me to watch how her body cycled up and down, but I was happy that the doctor was able to see a better version of Elizabeth that day. This visit provided us with additional options for my daughter.

The doctor was experimenting with other pharmaceuticals besides chemo. He suggested that Elizabeth try them, so she did. It was the last treatment plan that Elizabeth did and it was decidedly different. We had always treated her disease with chemotherapy and/or radiation. Now we were treating her with non-chemo drugs. There were a number of different drugs. One was for reducing high cholesterol and another was to reduce menstrual cramping. It was an odd combination of drugs. The pharmacy questioned why a seven year old would be taking these medicines. I was happy they did. They weren't drugs that a young child would normally take.

When she started the protocol, they were very hard on Elizabeth's body. We heard about an adult woman who was taking the same drug for menstrual cramps. She mentioned she would double over in pain from the medicine. She stated the drug was worse than the menstrual cramps she was trying to avoid!

Since Elizabeth was on this same drug for menstrual cramps, she experienced that same cramping and doubling over. Unfortunately, we had no choice but to continue giving it to her because this was the new protocol she was on. It was a horrific thing to have to administer these drugs knowing how she reacted to them.

One day she asked, "Mommy, when can I be done taking these medicines?"

I just couldn't bring myself to say, "Elizabeth, if you go off these medicines, you won't survive." So instead, I shrugged. It bothered me to know that the medicines were causing her so much pain.

That was the first time she asked to stop taking her medicines. She had taken so many medicines in her life. I thought, *Oh my gosh, I don't know if I can ever give her that gift of not taking medicine.* She kept on with her treatments without any more complaints.

No More Medicine

In June 2012, Elizabeth had the next MRI. After the MRI, we went back to the outpatient clinic to hear the results. When the doctor came in to consult with us, he said we had to go to another room. Someone from child life came in to stay with Elizabeth. I decided to stay with Elizabeth instead. I would get updated later from the other family members. The doctor wasn't happy about this but he went along with it.

It was the first time the doctor did not show the MRI images. They usually would bring up the photos whether it was good, bad, or indifferent. The doctor said that her cancer had spread all over her brain and spine. There were no more treatment options left. It was horrible news, but the one blessing, within the news, was Elizabeth was going to finally get her request. She would not have to take her medicines anymore.

It took a few months to have this happen because she had to be weaned off some of the drugs. Eventually she got off all the pharmaceuticals, just like she'd wanted months before.

I wasn't ready or capable of giving her that wish at the time, but it was something she got in those last months of her life. I am glad she was able to be off all those medicines finally.

The doctors told the other family members that there was nothing more they could do for her. They felt she had two weeks, and at most, two months to live.

This was on a Friday in June.

We took her home and I proceeded to stay up the whole weekend. I was not about to let her leave this Earth without me being present for it.

I did my darnedest to stay alert the entire weekend. Thankfully, she was still alive Monday morning. After being up all weekend, I was extremely strung out. I decided to call my church. The church had an emergency number to call. I wanted to talk to a priest. I left a message saying, "Is there any way that Elizabeth could get her first holy communion today?"

I explained the situation that she had finished one full year of the two-year process for first holy communion. I asked if the priest could make an exception in her case. Thankfully he did. He got there later that same day.

Together with the priest, we transformed the living room into an altar to perform the sacrament. He proceeded to do his first ever home First Holy Communion with my daughter. A handful of people gathered that evening for the ceremony. It was quite beautiful. Elizabeth was most comfortable in her pajamas, so we kept her in them for her communion. We had a simple meal at home with our family after the service was done.

Elizabeth had been asking to get communion ever since she could put the words together. She would see us receiving communion at mass and she would ask, "When is it my turn?" I knew that I needed to get her this sacrament and that's just what I did.

After Elizabeth received her First Holy Communion, there were a couple of dedicated Eucharistic ministers that brought Elizabeth communion daily. They continued coming all the months she survived.

Independence Day

A few weeks later, it was July 4th. Elizabeth had stopped most of her medicines. She was feeling much better, so we were able to go to the parade in Ridgewood, NJ. We got food at the pancake house. Boy, did Elizabeth love the cornbread there! It was such a wonderful day! We finished the day off with ice cream from her favorite ice cream shop.

First Day of School

Elizabeth didn't have the energy or strength to go to school in person anymore, but I still wanted her to have the experience of her first day. I took Elizabeth for a quick visit to her classroom. As we were walking down the hall to the classroom, kids kept saying "It's Elizabeth!" She was a celebrity.

When we went into the classroom, Elizabeth sat next to a kindergartener. Her class had kids from grades K-2. This little boy and Elizabeth hit it off. It was so nice for her to see all her classmates, teachers, and aides.

Picture Day

Elizabeth was able to get a non-traditional school picture. Mary's preschool offered for her siblings to join in her school picture. I brought Elizabeth and Anna to Mary's school. Once we got there, they suggested that all three girls do the photograph together. It was wonderful how accommodating they were to us.

Halloween

Elizabeth's favorite holiday was Halloween. Elizabeth and Anna were able to go to Mary's preschool trunk-or-treat. Elizabeth dressed up as one of her favorite things, a doctor! Getting to have the joy of another Halloween in her life was so special!

We were extra lucky to celebrate Halloween at the trunk-or-treat because the actual day of Halloween was canceled! Hurricane Sandy hit New Jersey on October 29, 2012. It flooded many towns and millions of people lost power.

We lost power at our house and moved in with Mommom and Poppy for a week. We needed a warm house to stay in while the power was being restored. Elizabeth and her sisters loved getting to stay at their grandparents' house. It was a vacation for them. Schools were closed for the whole week. There were fallen trees on the roads, making it hard to drive around. Thankfully Mommom and Poppy had power the whole time. We were so grateful to stay at their house.

Christmas 2012

During the 2012 Christmas season, we decorated extra early. It was only the beginning of December, and the Christmas decorations were up. This wasn't typical for us because I usually waited until after my December birthday to decorate.

We had a nice surprise when a local landscaping company offered to decorate the outside of our house with lights and a fresh cut Christmas tree. My girls enjoyed all the decorations!

Right around this time, Elizabeth's dad said to me, "You realize Elizabeth can't see the TV anymore?"

I said, "No, what do you mean?"

He asked me to observe her and I did. I then asked Elizabeth to tell me what was going on. She said that the TV was all blurry and she couldn't see it.

I said, "Elizabeth, you need to tell Mommy right away when something like this happens. Seimei can help with the blurriness." We had been doing a lot of Seimei on her every day and now we began to do even more. We made her eyesight the primary focus for her Seimei sessions.

A couple of days later we passed the Christmas tree in the house. She said, "Mommy, I can see the lights!" I choked up with tears of gratitude. Such a simple thing like seeing, which many of us take for granted, was back for Elizabeth. It was life-changing for me to know Elizabeth could see again. She got to see the Christmas lights! She just loved Christmas and now she was able to enjoy more of it. Thank you, Seimei!

Closer to Christmas, the Mary Therese Rose Fund elves came to deliver Christmas gifts to all three of my girls. What a great surprise! We were also blessed with another group of people asking me what the girls wanted for Christmas. Elizabeth had asked for a CT scanner. It was a machine that looked like a big donut with a table in the middle. Well, I am not sure how they did it, but they delivered a handmade wooden replica of a CT scanner. Wow! A Christmas miracle!

New Year's

A few days before New Year's Eve, Elizabeth lost the ability to swallow. I was determined to still try and get some nutrients in her. One of the last things I tried was a syringe. I would suction up some water and put it in her mouth. That wasn't even working. Her brain wasn't communicating correctly with the nerves in her mouth. She just wasn't able to swallow. I asked for even more support from the Seimei community.

We worked round-the-clock for those last few days of 2012. When she woke up on New Year's Day, she ate and drank four meals as though she'd never had any problem swallowing! I was so thankful!

Going to see Rudy

She was rallying for a few weeks. Then towards the end of January, she said to my neighbor and me, "I want to go see Rudy in Heaven." Rudy, whom Elizabeth adored, had died in January 2011. Elizabeth had said similar things about Rudy in the past to me.

I would always reply to her, "Not before you're 104!"

But this time when she said it, my neighbor replied. She said to Elizabeth, "Elizabeth, you can visit Rudy anytime you want in your dreams."

Elizabeth just politely repeated "I want to go see Rudy in Heaven." She repeated this many times. She never corrected anyone, she just reiterated "I want to go see Rudy in Heaven."

Later that night, when it was just her and I, I told her "Mommy will keep doing Seimei forever for you, but it is your body and it is your choice."

The following three days, Tuesday, Wednesday, and Thursday, she stopped eating and drinking. I also didn't offer her anything because I was trying to honor the choice she had made.

Friends and family started flooding in because we thought she would be gone very soon. On Thursday night, her uncle was holding her. He said to her, "Elizabeth, do you want some water?"

Elizabeth said, "Yes."

Her uncle got her some water and she drank it. That gave me hope again.

I said, "Oh wow, she drank some water!"

The next morning, I woke up early to a beautiful sunrise. I decided to do a Seimei session for her while she was still sleeping. After working on her, I had this inner knowing. I knew that no matter whether Elizabeth lived or died, both she and I were going to be okay.

That shifted everything for me. I had been a basket case since Monday night when I had given her permission to leave. I had thought, *Oh no, what did I just give her permission to do?* But thankfully giving her a Seimei session that Friday morning had changed everything.

I was given this amazing gift of knowing that somehow, some way, no matter if she lived or died, both she and I were going to be okay. A girlfriend came over a few hours later. I was so excited to tell her about what had happened and how different I felt.

I started to explain to her this experience I had, and she said, "You don't have to explain it to me. I was here two days ago. I saw how distraught you were. As soon as I walked into your house today, I not only saw a change in you. I saw a change in Elizabeth."

I thought, *Wow, how incredible.* I hadn't been able to remember who came to see Elizabeth on Tuesday, Wednesday, and Thursday of that week. I didn't realize that my girlfriend had been there a couple of days earlier. It was a beautiful gift that she could reflect to me what a change she saw. What a pleasure that was!

Elizabeth started eating and drinking again. She wasn't a picky eater anymore. She ate the healthiest foods she had ever eaten in her life. She was no longer asking for all her favorite fast foods and candies. I picked the healthiest and most wonderful things for her to eat. I hoped that her healthy eating might have been the extra thing that kept her here.

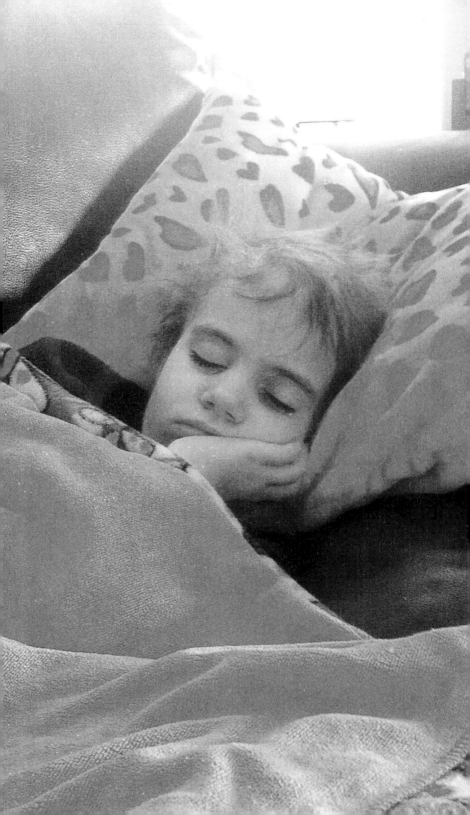

Diet Plan

In January 2013, a friend told us about the Budwig diet. There was a belief that this diet could help cancer patients. The Budwig diet would have the cancer patient blend cottage cheese, honey and flaxseed oil. The patient needed to take it daily at a minimum. The patient should also eat lots of fruits and vegetables.

Another friend gave us an organic wild blueberry smoothie recipe. I would make the smoothie and the Budwig blend daily. Elizabeth loved the smoothie but she didn't like the Budwig blend. I would negotiate with Elizabeth to eat it and I promised her that I would eat any of the leftover amounts. There would always be leftovers, so I knew first-hand why Elizabeth had trouble finishing it.

Each spoonful was harder and harder to swallow because it would accumulate in my throat. I know this was happening to Elizabeth too, so I couldn't blame her when she only ate a small amount. I was grateful to have something for Elizabeth to try.

Valentine's Day

Elizabeth woke up early on Valentine's Day. I noticed that there was a pool of blood in her ear. It startled me. I'd never seen something like that with her before, so I called the visiting nurse.

I asked, "What's going on?"

The visiting nurse said, "Well, the pressure is building in her head from the tumors, which is making the capillaries burst. That's why you are seeing the blood in her ear. This is going to continue until she dies."

I said, "Thank you for that information, but I need to please get off the line now. I need to call my Seimei teacher." We got off the line and I called immediately. I asked my Seimei teacher, "Okay, what are we going to do?"

She explained what I needed to do in person with Elizabeth and she also started working from a distance. Within twenty to thirty minutes, the bleeding stopped. Never again did she have that symptom.

What a blessing to not have to see my daughter bleed each day for the rest of her life!

Seimei Baths

Seimei baths were a huge help to Elizabeth. I gave Elizabeth Seimei baths daily. When Elizabeth was in the Seimei bath, she would get little bubbles all over her skin. It was fascinating to see! Those bubbles were toxins actively purging from her skin!

In January 2013, Elizabeth no longer was moving her right arm. Suddenly, one day, her right arm bent up and then straightened out again and again. I was concerned about this unusual movement, so I brought her upstairs for a Seimei bath. As soon as she got into the Seimei bath, her right arm relaxed. The involuntary movements never happened again! Amazing!

During February and March 2013, I took the Seimei bath with Elizabeth. She was too weak to support herself in the bath. I would get in with my bathing suit on and she would rest on me as I bathed her.

Her Breath

Jenny, a volunteer from camp, was holding Elizabeth in her arms on Sunday afternoon. She had come to visit us for the weekend. Suddenly, Elizabeth stopped breathing. Elizabeth had been having pauses in her breath for a while now so I wasn't alarmed. This pause was longer than usual. Jenny asked me if Elizabeth's pauses in her breath usually lasted that long. I told her no.

I called a friend and she said I could do CPR to revive her. I chose not to because I wanted to honor the time that Elizabeth chose to leave.

Nine months earlier, her dad and I had filled out a do-not-resuscitate order for Elizabeth. We couldn't do it right away. What an awful thing for a parent to have to fill out. It should never be something a parent does for a child. I hope one day it never will need to be done again for a child. Unfortunately, it was a requirement of the visiting nurses' service.

I called the visiting nurse service. While we waited for the nurse to arrive, Elizabeth's uncle suggested we give her one final bath. He and I gave Elizabeth a sponge bath. We dressed her in comfy pajamas. She loved to be in pajamas! Some family and close friends gathered at our home. The nurse came and pronounced the death of Elizabeth. We called our local funeral home.

A few hours later, the funeral home came to take Elizabeth. This was one of the hardest things for me to do. I had cared for Elizabeth 24/7 for the last six and a half years of her illness. In an instant, I was off duty.

I wasn't sure how I was going to continue. Thank goodness I was a mom of three children. My Mary and my Anna gave me a reason to get out of bed. They were four and almost two years old. On my worst days of grief, when I didn't think I could function, the girls would be asking for their breakfast. I had to pull together all my strength and carry on. Thank goodness for my girls!

Elizabeth's Celebration of Life

March 10, 2013 was the day Elizabeth left this world. We held a two-day wake for her on March 12th and 13th. On March 14th, we had her funeral. We were very fortunate that our church let us hold the wake and funeral at the church. Thousands of people came. People stood in line for hours to pay their respects. Some people didn't even make it through to see us.

Friends and family helped to search for digital photos on our phones, the computer, and social media. We had a huge compilation of pictures to share with everyone at the wake and funeral.

Multiple digital photo frames cycled through beautiful pictures of my daughter and significant moments in her life.

Another friend said, "Don't worry about the repass. I'm going to make centerpieces for the tables." She knew that Elizabeth's favorite color was red, so she made the centerpieces with gorgeous red silk flowers.

We had the church choir sing most of the funeral songs but we also had a musician friend come to play at the end of the funeral. Elizabeth's dad gave the eulogy.

My cousins made red ribbon bracelets and tied tiny bells on them. Everyone that came to the services received one of these bracelets. Elizabeth, as a little girl, had bells tied to her shoes so we would always know where she was. The bells on the bracelets would constantly remind us of her.

A friend told me that she leaves a bracelet on the rearview mirror of her car. Any time when she's having a tough moment, she taps the bracelet and asks Elizabeth for help.

Another friend told me that her bracelet had gone missing but it suddenly appeared on her mat when she returned home. How in the world did it get there? Elizabeth finds a way to make her presence known. I bet that friend needed a sign from her that day.

There was a beautiful display of balloons for the funeral from a friend. She created a balloon arch in the shape of a rainbow, using all the different colors. We got special permission from the priest to have those balloons on the altar during the funeral mass.

She was just a child, so having those balloons during the funeral was perfect. We called Elizabeth's funeral a celebration of her life. We wanted people to remember the joy, not the harder times. We wanted them to celebrate the seven years we had Elizabeth with us.

As time went on, we got balloons on dates significant to Elizabeth. We sent the balloons up to heaven with little notes to her.

Eucharist

Since Eucharistic ministers had helped Elizabeth, it was an area where I wanted to give back. I went through the process of becoming a Eucharistic Minister. I started doing house visits for those recovering from surgery and those that were close to their death.

I was able to bring them communion when they weren't able to get to mass. It was great to pay forward what had been done for Elizabeth.

Bereavement Weekends

About six months after Elizabeth died, there was a bereavement weekend at camp. I wanted to go and share what I do with Seimei.

The camp social worker declined my offer to do Seimei for the camp session. She felt that my first time back to camp would be hard on me, and she was right. I hadn't realized how hard it was going to be at camp without Elizabeth. I also hadn't realized how hard it was going to be to see people who knew Elizabeth and our family. When the staff and volunteers saw us, they expressed a look of shock. They would say, "Why are you here?" before realizing exactly why we were there. Thankfully, everyone was unfailingly supportive. It was where we needed to be.

During the weekend, we wrote messages on balloons. Camp would do a balloon launch for all the families and volunteers that have lost children. It was incredible to see a huge volume of balloons all going up to heaven at once. Not too many dry eyes there.

We attended the bereavement weekends every year since Elizabeth died. The camp social worker was correct about waiting to share Seimei that first time at bereavement camp. I started doing Seimei the second time I attended a bereavement weekend. I was there as a bereaved family member, but also volunteered at the family breaks to do Seimei for the other parents and volunteers. The staff was helpful. They always made sure I would have a quiet place to do Seimei for the adults.

Five years after my daughter died, I decided that I would start going to camp as a full-time volunteer. I chose two camp sessions that had children battling cancer. I wanted to connect with other cancer families and help them. We also went to bereavement camp, so the girls and I were going three times a year now.

As a full-time volunteer, I worked with the adults, offering Seimei during the breaks in their schedule. It was so rewarding to be helping parents that were going through the cancer journey with their children. It was also great to help the volunteers that were working with the children. I had first-hand knowledge of the cancer journey and it was helpful to the parents.

The girls were thrilled to hear that we were a volunteer family. They loved to camp and knew this would get us there more. Once they found out that there was no limit to how many weeks we volunteered, they asked if we could go every week! That would have been loads of fun if only we could have pulled it off.

I'm so appreciative to have camp be part of my journey with Elizabeth and the rest of my family. We have gained many friends and memories that I will treasure forever.

CHAPTER EIGHT

Seimei In My Life Today

Seimei has become an integral part of my life. It has helped me recover from the cancer journey with Elizabeth and repair from the grief of a world without Elizabeth. The road hasn't been easy without her. There have been people that have fallen out of my life. A saving grace has been those that stayed with me during this long haul. Another has been those that have come into my life after Elizabeth died.

I am eternally blessed to have had Elizabeth for almost eight years. I am equally blessed to have my other daughters, Mary and Anna, to enjoy many more years together.

It has been eleven years since I learned Seimei and the gifts of this practice continued to bless me. We have a strong Seimei community where we help each other when issues arise in our lives. We also celebrate each of our triumphs.

Our biggest annual celebration is a birthday party for Seimei's founder, Hiraki Kaiso. We bring special Japanese foods and desserts for the party. We also do kind acts as a thank you to our founder. I am not sure where I would be today without Seimei in my life.

When I speak about Elizabeth it continues her legacy. I want to share her story with everyone. I also want people to know what an amazing difference Seimei made in her life. The more people that know about Seimei, the better.

I believe if I had found Seimei at the beginning of her cancer battle, she would be here telling her story herself. Why not give the gift of introducing Seimei to someone else? It may just save a life.

For more information, please visit my website at

www.seimeihealing.com

CHAPTER NINE

Resources and Charities

Seimei Foundation seimeifoundation.org

Seimei Foundation offers both online and in-person programming to experience the many facets of Seimei.

Camp Sunshine campsunshine.org

Camp Sunshine is a retreat for children with life-threatening illnesses and their families. They also provide bereavement programs for those prior Camp Sunshine families that have lost a child.

Tomorrow's Children's Fund (TCF) tcfkid.org

TCF assists families that have children battling cancer and serious blood disorders. TCF provides a loving environment for children in treatment and a full scope of services to relieve families' emotional and financial stress. TCF provides activities, events, outings, parties, and more. They include support for families post-treatment and those that lost a child.

Mary Therese Rose Fund (MTRF) marythereserose.org

MTRF helps children with disabilities live the joys of childhood to the fullest despite their limitations. They offer many programs. Saturday Stars, Mary's Closet, hippotherapy, reimbursement of medical costs and a recreation program.

Children's Brain Tumor Foundation (CBTF) cbtf.org

CBTF provides counseling and fun events for families whose child is fighting cancer, families whose child is in remission, and families who lost a child.

Cancer Care cancercare.org

Cancer Care provides counseling to help during the cancer battle as well as for the families that lost a loved one to cancer. They also provide a weekend camp for grieving families.

Good Grief good-grief.org

Good Grief provides counseling to help families that have lost a child. They offer weekly support as well as a week-long summer camp.

Comfort Zone Camp comfortzonecamp.org

Comfort Zone Camp offers a fun, safe place for grieving children.

Momcology momcology.org

Momcology offers online and in-person peer programs for families effected by childhood cancer.

The Still Place thestillplace.org

The Still Place provides rest, renewal, and re-creation to families with children affected by serious illness or loss.

Acknowledgments

I want to acknowledge all my family, friends, community members, and professionals that have helped me in the journey with Elizabeth, in its aftermath, and with writing this book.

Some helped to pick up Mary from preschool and helped watch Anna while Mary was in school. Sometimes watching both my younger girls when I needed to take Elizabeth to the hospital.

Meals were brought to us and kind acts were done whether we knew you or not.

Friends and family would visit us at the hospital and help lighten our tedious day. They would also rally around us during MRI and surgery days. A group of family members would come to the hospital and spend the entire day with us. Others would celebrate each of Elizabeth's MRIs, no matter what the results were.

I'm so grateful for the whole blood and platelet direct donations you all did for Elizabeth. Whole blood donations take ten to fifteen minutes. Platelet donations take about an hour. Amazingly, many people donated multiple times. A very detailed log was taken on the day each person donated. That allowed us to inform the specific donor when their blood product had been used by Elizabeth.

My colleagues encouraged me to write this book. It took a lot of convincing and many years until I was ready to write. I appreciate all who said I should.

 You know who you are.